Praise for *Thinking Therapeuti*

Tom Barber and Sandra Westland offer an e
to the hypnotherapy profession with their new book, *Thinking Therapeutically: Hypnotic Skills and Strategies Explored*. Rather than presenting detailed and lengthy explanations of various techniques, they provide numerous case histories showing how they use different techniques for different clients. Their practice offers a blend of both NLP and traditional hypnotherapy, combined with various imagery techniques. Their book includes scripts from actual sessions with clients who experienced guided affective imagery, hypnoanalysis, regression, parts therapy and dream work, as well as various NLP techniques.

There are usually different ways to arrive at the same destination, so Tom Barber and Sandra Westland show how they use a variety of techniques to help clients achieve their desired results. The authors also use some metaphors quite skilfully. Their case history involving dream work was especially interesting to me because of my very limited experience with dreams. On a personal note, I was impressed at the honesty of the authors to include a chapter on their own personal journeys into the hypnotherapy profession.

Roy Hunter, PhD, FAPHP, author of *The Art of Hypnosis,*
The Art of Hypnotherapy, Mastering the Power of Self-Hypnosis
and *Hypnosis for Inner Conflict Resolution*

Here at last is the book that I wish had been available when I first started out in practice. The authors understand totally that a newly trained practitioner, whilst assumed by the client to be the consummate professional, is in reality in every sense a novice – and only too aware of it. In order to fully engage with the reader, they willingly (indeed necessarily) expose themselves and their respective therapeutic approaches to scrutiny and, in so doing, display exceptional professional generosity.

Not satisfied with the mediocre, the authors are concerned with demonstrating the full potential of what can be achieved via a range of hypnotherapeutic interventions. Using actual case examples, and with an obvious passion for their calling, they illustrate via an engaging mix of real time therapist/client dialogue and explanatory comment on both their own questions and the client responses, exactly what worked and, on occasions, what did not.

In essence they convey that most essential of commodities to the practising hypnotherapist – confidence in his or her own ability to provide the service that the client both has paid for and expects. In so doing, they show the novice practitioner how to maintain a steady hand at the tiller no matter how stormy the passage may become.

Although presumably intended for the student and newly qualified practitioner, this is a book that should be in every hypnotherapist's library regardless of their experience in practice.

William Broom, Chief Executive,
General Hypnotherapy Standards Council
and General Hypnotherapy Register

Tom and Sandra convey a sense of how it feels to grow therapy within the framework of the well-formed techniques and approaches they present in this book. Processing the sessions in the way they have shows therapy developing creatively and engenders trust that there is always another perspective to be found. I was most touched by the intimacy of disclosure showing the clear advantage we gain as therapists when we acknowledge our own journeys, experiences and responses. In *Thinking Therapeutically* both experience and awareness are demonstrated in ways that can be referred to by individual students or groups; even practising therapists will be guided to revisit core skills that easily fall to the side as they take on more methods and techniques in the always developing and brave world of integrative therapy.

Bobby Keeling, Adv Dip.Hyp/Psych and NLP Practitioner

Congratulations to Tom Barber and Sandra Westland for producing this outstanding and unique book which has relevance to all who work within the field of hypnotherapy, beginners and experienced practitioners alike.

Tom and Sandra are two of our most experienced and respected practitioners who also have that superb talent of communication at all levels. The book, a 'must have' for all those interested in hypnotherapy, not only describes the journeys that have been made to becoming therapists but also includes a fascinating journey into their own professional world where real-life situations are recounted and dissected. It is almost like a 'fly on the wall' documentary and is totally riveting from beginning to end.

Seldom has one seen such openness and honesty. There is an immediacy in their writing, although they have differing styles, and one feels very much part of the whole experience and, as such, derives a great deal of benefit from what they share so ably with us. It makes no difference whether you are a student or a seasoned professional, there is most definitely something here for everyone to appreciate at their own level.

The authors share with us some of their most memorable sessions which they both analyse and criticise as they go on. Each session is processed and analysed critically and honestly. As one reads it becomes an exercise in which the reader becomes totally involved and formulates his/her own opinions and strategies, often putting themselves in the position of the therapist and planning their own route forwards.

It is one thing having strategies explained in a dry, clinical way but it is totally another to have the strategy theoretically explained and then, through the medium of the verbatim reporting of sessions, actually put to real use in such an open and compelling way. At times their clients almost become yours as you share each intense moment of the journey made.

This superb book gives the reader not only the theories, the strategies, the techniques and the approaches but also accompanies all of these with personal expert guidance and consideration which takes us from the general to the particular with all our clients.

The reader is engaged in sessions which are far ranging – from driving test nerves to bulimia. We examine the world of hypnohealing and hypnoanalysis. We become involved in the fascinating world of parts therapy and the transforming effect of the SWISH technique. We explore the world of the inner child and learn how to access it.

There is such fascination here. Such inspiration. Such intense and, at times, deeply moving, reality and humanity. It is a book which does NOT deserve a place on your bookshelf but a regular place in your hands, on your desk and in your mind. The shelf suggests dormancy. This book deserves to be part of your everyday action and thought.

This is seeing hypnotherapy in action and, with the honesty and transparency already mentioned, we see it warts and all, as it were. There is honest explanation of what worked and what didn't in the sessions described. On reading I certainly had many of my own experiences springing to mind, comparing and contrasting what I did to the way the authors had worked. I am glad to say that most of the time the roads travelled were very close to each other, but there were times when elements of doubt or disagreement crept in. This I feel helps to emphasise that therapy hinges not just around the strategies and techniques but also on the unique make-up of the therapist too. There are times when we really need to stand back and look not just at the client but at ourselves too, and not be afraid to question our own approaches and be prepared to amend and adapt where necessary.

The book is both inspirational and creative. It is instructive and engaging. Above all it is unerringly honest and that is a major part of its appeal.

I have no hesitation in recommending this to all training establishments, students and practitioners, old and new. This is a book which, to date, has no peer. In all seriousness, you cannot afford to be without it!

I feel that this book deserves the highest acclaim by students and fellow professionals alike and I, for one, hope that we see more books in years to come from these two enlightened and enlightening professionals.

**David Slater BA, DHyp, MHA(RegHyp), MASC, DCS, MGSCT,
Clinical Hypnotherapist and Counsellor**

Thinking Therapeutically by Tom Barber and Sandra Westland affords a rare look into the minds of two seasoned hypnotherapists as they relate case studies and comment on one another's work. This book is ideal for beginning hypnotherapists and for those who wonder about a therapist's internal process during the therapeutic conversation.

The authors open the book by each telling the personal story of how he/she came to be a therapist, reflecting on life-changing experiences as well as an existentialist philosophy. From that point, Barber and Westland alternate authorship in the subsequent chapters. The reader learns that these authors are highly eclectic hypnotherapists, drawing from a wide variety of approaches.

Each section presents a single client session and is built around this format:

- A description of a particular therapeutic method, citing authors who have written about the method.

- How the author applied the method in a session with a client. The author explains the rationale for selecting *this* method for *this* client, with consideration of the client's presenting issue and what the client wants as an outcome. Excerpts of session transcripts are provided, with the therapist's running commentary.

- The other author's comments on the session.

- 'What happened next' – a follow-up on what the client did after the session.

I liked the authors' expert descriptions and real-life applications of a wide variety of interventions that are a hypnotherapist's stock-in-trade: anchoring, SWISH pattern, parts work, guided imagery, dream analysis, regression, hypnoanalysis, and inner-child work. The descriptions are so clear, readers can easily model them. In fact, the day I read about 'the library' regression method, I used it on a client with success! The authors explain how to apply these methods to a wide range of typical, yet often challenging, issues such as agoraphobia, shyness, internal conflict, irritable bowel syndrome, bulimia and overeating.

The book is reminiscent of the conversation between Milton H. Erickson and Ernest Rossi in the classic, *The February Man*. The two authors take turns explaining their selection of interventions, perceptions of their clients, feelings during the session and evaluation of each outcome. What I found most touching was the honesty with which the authors shared their perceptions and emotions during each session, even when they were uncertain as to how to proceed.

Reading the book, in between therapy sessions with my own clients, I found myself commenting on each session along with the authors, as well as reflecting more closely on my own internal process as a therapist. The book made me realise two things. First, how much we, as therapists, need one another as sounding boards. Second, how much being a therapist differs from most other occupations in that we bring to our work not only our skills, but elements of our selves – our own histories and emotions. It's always amazing to me how we, as therapists, manage to tread the fine line between professional objectivity and the ability to be fully in rapport with clients expressing and exploring their most private emotions and thoughts. Barber and Westland describe that process with remarkable precision.

Judith E. Pearson, PhD
Psychotherapist, Coach, NLP/Hypnotherapy Practitioner
and Trainer

Thinking Therapeutically gives you a solid run through a range of effective hypnosis and NLP approaches and techniques. Unlike other books that become compendiums of marginal strategies, the authors focus on those approaches most likely to help the client. Regression, parts, imagery and NLP's most important techniques are all called on to help the client improve. Every therapist will find value herein. Pick up this book and keep it at the ready in your office.

Kevin Hogan, PsyD, author of *The New Hypnotherapy Handbook* **and** *Tinnitus: Turning the Volume Down*

As therapists who are also dedicated trainers it is no surprise that Tom and Sandra have produced a book with rich perceptions of the therapeutic process. The reader is given a candid, open peephole into the therapy room, where Tom and Sandra share their successes, fears, feelings and insights; not to mention their 'compare and contrast' comments of one another's sessions. Novice and seasoned therapists alike can benefit from this rare opportunity to learn from and reflect on the practical and emotional journey within the therapy room for both the client and the therapist.

Penny Parks, author of *Rescuing the Inner Child* **and** *The Counsellor's Guide to Parks Inner Child Therapy*

Thinking
Therapeutically

Thinking Therapeutically

Hypnotic Skills and Strategies Explored

Tom Barber and Sandra Westland

Crown House Publishing Limited

www.crownhouse.co.uk

www.crownhousepublishing.com

First published by

Crown House Publishing Ltd
Crown Buildings, Bancyfelin, Carmarthen, Wales, SA33 5ND, UK
www.crownhouse.co.uk

and

Crown House Publishing Company LLC
6 Trowbridge Drive, Suite 5, Bethel, CT 06801-2858, USA
www.crownhousepublishing.com

© Tom Barber and Sandra Westland 2011

British Library Cataloguing-in-Publication Data
A catalogue entry for this book is available
from the British Library.

ISBN 978-184590677-1

LCCN 2010937323

Printed and bound in the UK by
Bell & Bain Ltd, Glasgow

Acknowledgements

This book is dedicated to all our clients and students – past, present and future – who continually inspire us with their courage and educate us in being and becoming more mindful therapists.

We would like to thank Sandy Davies for his unlimited faith and certainty that this book was possible and for his unwavering support in our passion to build The Contemporary College of Therapeutic Studies, and also to Tanya Colley, who had the unenviable task of editing our very first draft!

Sandra: I personally would like to acknowledge Joyce Munson (my mum) and my good friends who simply and unconditionally believe in me and support me in my life, whatever I am striving for. I dedicate this book to you all as your belief in me has been, and is, unquestionable.

Tom: I would like to acknowledge my family and friends who, I am sure, wonder with curiosity what I do for hours on end in my office. This is it! To my grandchildren, James and Oliver, I dedicate this book to you both, to inspire you on your journeys through life, knowing that anything is possible.

And finally to the memory of Arthur Munson and Mick Barber, our fathers, who always encouraged us to reach high for our dreams and never stop reaching. We wish you were both here to see the fruits of your faith.

Contents

Introduction

When the idea for this book was born, our intention was to provide a practical resource for those embarking on the journey of becoming a hypnotherapist. Throughout our experience of training therapists, we so often hear questions beginning with 'How do I …?', 'What if …?' and 'When do I ..?' These searching questions don't simply disappear for therapists once they are qualified. No matter how thorough a training programme is the newly qualified therapist in practice, is still, well … new, and yet place themselves exclusively as the sole 'knowing being' in front of a client. Traditionally, the therapist is considered the 'authority figure' within a therapeutic relationship – deemed the expert in what to do, when to do it and where to go in the process of therapy. Meanwhile, the client invests time, money and energy in their treatment, and places themself, often without question, into the assumed safety of the therapist's hands, expecting them to facilitate some kind of change.

When first immersed in professional practice, a lack of essential experience is a given and is something that we, as trainers and supervisors, encounter regularly. We have noticed that *feeling* inexperienced seems to be a key factor in the potential practitioner becoming an actual practitioner. We want to reach out to those starting on the journey into professional practice; igniting possibilities and creating enthusiasm for the artistic, exciting and often deeply moving world of integrative hypnotherapy and psychotherapy. In this, we also hope to potentially enable the established practitioner to step even further into the realms of self-exploration and development.

Our passion in the training of therapists is driven by a deep desire to inspire those entering this rewarding profession to be all they can be. In this book, we share our experiences of being a hypnotherapist, familiarising you with what we consider to be some of the most effective hypnotic strategies and techniques currently available. Furthermore, we want to allude to our own personal worlds of internal therapeutic processing, which all therapists are encouraged to develop and listen to. It will be hard not to find yourself drifting into your own search, exploring and reflecting on what *you* might have done in the therapeutic situations in which we found ourselves. In short, this book is about enhancing creative imagination and exploring what can be achieved through therapy.

Where we have come from and our journeys into the therapeutic world are followed by examples of our client work. Each case begins with an introduction to the techniques used and then explores the client and their presenting problem, followed by the initial exploration, the hypnotic intervention and the processing of the session. Alongside this, there is post-session reflection and an account of the future work that was planned. We aim to demonstrate how a variety of hypnotic interventions can help clients to move towards empowerment and their own creative freedom. In providing the directional stepping-stones that are naturally missing at an early stage of a therapist's professional development, we hope to inform the personal passage of individuals into the world of integrative therapy. We explore our perspectives, questioning what has transpired and its meaning in relation to the therapist and the client, founded in different gender perspectives and our distinctive personal and professional journeys, which will no doubt be compared, contrasted and criticised. We hope in reading this book that you will do all three.

From the many client hours we have had the privilege to be part of, there have been countless memorable sessions that could have been included in this book and so the process of choosing just nine was a difficult but enlightening one. In respect of the permissions for the client examples in the book, which are based on real work from our therapy practices, we have recreated the dialogue from each session, disguising any identifying features of the client or their lives in a way that we hope both honours and respects their right to anonymity. In the case of client material that is a near accurate representation of the session, express permission has been sought and granted. Other sessions have been altered slightly or combined with other sessions to ensure the client material is unidentifiable.

Sandra found the sessions she chose seemed to move the client towards a greater awareness, in which they became excited at the new possibilities open to them. In particular she found a sense of connectedness, a feeling of being immersed in the client's world. Above all, what captured her about these sessions was that they showed the client's discovery of themselves and of a sense of hope that things could be different.

In Tom's sessions, he was aware of the noticeable struggles within each of his clients, often feeling that they were yearning for more of him than it was actually possible to give in therapy. In certain cases he felt that some of the previous sessions with these clients could quite easily be used as a demonstration of what *not* to do in therapy. He chose these sessions, however, as he was conscious that they brought about a personal connection with his clients. For him, they show that even when therapy feels like it is a struggle, 'holding' the situation and trusting in the process of therapy will eventually lead the client to where they need to go.

As you would expect, when two uniquely individual therapists come together to write a book about how to 'do' and 'be' (thera-peutically), and the thought processes that underpin this work, the inevitable long discussions, debates and deliberations immersed us in a deeper sense of what it really means to be a therapist. We hope this book has evolved not only into a practical helpful guide, but also into an exploration of the deeper questions that are raised when one's beliefs, values and therapeutic work are challenged by another. Thus we hope it is a book of substance, with the intention of challenging the reader's therapeutic journey and inspiring the potential of using hypnosis. With this in mind, this book is aimed at those who are in or who have completed therapeutic training and hence are able to follow and use the techniques safely, ethically and therapeutically.

In Chapter 1, we share our personal stories and some of our previous life experiences prior to becoming therapists. We discuss what it was like starting out and why we have become so passionate about what we do. Our reason for writing about this is to offer you insight into not only how it was for us moving out of one career into the therapeutic world, but also to give you some insight into ourselves, to offer you a context within which to work from when you are reading our client sessions. In knowing something about us we hope to help you immerse yourself further into each session with a 'sense' of where each therapist and client was operating from. In Chapter 2, we describe three different sessions covering cognitive behavioural hypnotherapy and neurolinguistic program-ming (NLP), showing the effectiveness of specific 'quick change' techniques within a treatment. Chapter 3 focuses on the use of imagery to enhance awareness and to creatively and symbolically empower and heal the client. In Chapter 4 we demonstrate how exploring the root of the client's problem can help them to reorganise their world, freeing them from the binds and shackles of the past.

During our description of the sessions you may come across therapeutic terminology that is unfamiliar. Rather than interfering with the flow of the sessions or the internal process of you, the reader, we have included a glossary of terms towards the end of the book to describe *our* meanings within *our* discourse.

We hope you gain from this book as much as we have in writing it.

Chapter 1

The Journey to Becoming a Hypnotherapist

Tom's Beginning

It was with deep dissatisfaction in my working life, even at the age of 21, coupled with a dread at the thought of working for another forty years in the same job, which prompted me to look for something more in life. Work until that point had been varied, not mundane, but it was definitely lacking the sense of satisfaction and stimulation that I so yearned for. I grew up dreaming and craving excitement, imagining this ultimate exhilaration would come from becoming a soldier; and sensing this was my destiny, at the age of 16 I found myself in the ranks of the elite Junior Leaders Regiment of the Royal Engineers.

Arrival into the world of the British army exposed me to the fascinating diversity of human beings. I began, in a place of 'strange friends', to witness the resilience that individuals muster as they are challenged to their physical, mental and emotional limits. I watched young men forced into accelerated manhood, myself included; I survived the experience owing to an ability to adapt and conform learnt years earlier. When I look back on those times, and my undoubted resilience, I recognise with clarity what for me back then, and still is, the most precious of all human gifts – hope.

Even at this young impressionable age, I had a philosophical perspective on life, believing that everything happened for a reason. This was borne out while I was fulfilling my childhood ambition of jumping from a plane – floating through the air with nothing but a parachute to save me. In that moment, as my body gave out and my knees buckled upon landing, I knew this dream career was not meant to be. I had to quit. A year later my army friends departed for Iraq, some never to return. I was not one of them.

Leaving the army was a difficult and at times confusing process as I'd never had to consider myself as a member of the public. Integrating into civilian society, where it felt like nobody cared about anybody else was far from easy and both inner and outer conflicts quickly ensued. From building sites to plush sales offices, I scrambled to find something resembling true meaning in my daily routine, and with each job came the challenge of trying to settle down to the life that I thought was supposed to be lived. At 21 I was wholly frustrated and realised I just couldn't continue with this existence. I began to have a sense of feeling trapped. Trapped in nothing.

It was at this time that I came across an advertisement in an obscure magazine, picked up while waiting anxiously in a dentist's waiting room for that most gruesome and terrifying ordeal … a filling. I was desperate for a momentary distraction. 'Hypnotherapy and Counselling Courses' – that sounded different! What did it involve? Helping people – that could be worthwhile, I mused. Little did I realise what my request for this course information would lead to, or indeed how it would change my life.

It is strange sometimes how we find a calling in the most unlikely of places. That visit to the dentist, seeing an advert and responding to it changed everything for me, as eighteen months later, I qualified as an analytical hypnotherapist, ready to work with people and their problems. I thank my tutors to this day for giving me a belief in what I was doing and instilling in me the confidence to start out in this profession. Their words 'trust in the process' will remain forever etched in my mind.

I was surprised at how much of my early career as a therapist had disappeared somewhere into the realms of my distant memory when the formulation of this book took place. I have explained to students on many occasions how I now cringe at some of the things I used to say to clients; because back then therapy, for me, *was* a panacea and I fully expected to be able to help each client achieve what they wanted from our sessions. I was pretty secure in my knowledge and embraced a simplistic innocence in my work. There was no reason that I could think of why therapy would not work. 'Why would somebody consider entering therapy and not expect a successful outcome?', I would ask myself.

What was it like, the first few steps on this journey with clients? There is one word that encompasses the true basis of my thoughts and feelings back then, and that is *faith*. I felt assured and confident within the process and the power of therapy. I had faith in the new ways of thinking that I was offering to clients and in the techniques that I had in my therapeutic toolbox that once taught to them would help them move towards how they wanted to be.

This eagerness and belief, coupled with what I had learnt, brought a steady stream of clients through my door and I was always grateful that every client I worked with seemed to experience so much more than they bargained for. For me it was not *if* therapy would work, just *how* it could be shaped to work for each new and uniquely different person.

My fascination with human nature was also being nourished along the way, as I explored with clients why they and others behaved in such different and (for me) unpredictable ways. I too was searching for those answers and in need of more, which drew me to further training in advanced hypnotherapy, hypnohealing and stress counselling, where I gained more insight into the symptoms and reactions my clients were experiencing. I further studied person-centred counselling as I recognised a desire to work at more depth and as this unfolded in the therapy sessions, my connections with clients felt more meaningful, as did our communication, and from here my fascination with language was born. This curiosity guided me to find out more about how people interact with each other, and hence training in neurolinguistic programming (NLP) continued my voyage of discovery.

This absorbing and varied training certainly helped to build a more solid foundation to my work and after some years of giving therapy, a colleague and I were asked to travel to China to teach hypnotherapy to students at Sichuan University. This was, as you can imagine, a terrifying prospect, but it was the beginning of a whole new perspective on the world of therapy and over the following two years, I was privileged to teach hypnotherapy around the world – in Los Angeles, St Petersburg and Paris.

Reflecting on how my therapeutic career started reminds me how this profession is different for everyone – drawing from us the unique experiences and circumstances of our lives. Looking back has provided me with some illuminating insights into why I found this path, and as I consider now, knowing more of and about myself, I can touch a younger me who struggled to connect with people. In becoming a therapist, I began to connect with others and began to connect with my own sense of presence and existence, something I was quietly yearning to do.

The more clients I saw, the more I became aware of experiencing myself 'in the moment' with them, moving me to a place of greater unknowingness and, I guess it could be said, a greater purity with the client in front of me. I started to live in the very second of the session, and then the next second, and then the next. Indeed, life slowed down – and the sessions slowed down.

It was from this exploration that my innocence was revealed to me, and in some ways shattered, as I set myself in motion towards experiences and experiencing. This was where the real quest in being a therapist began; not questioning *what to do* with clients but *how to be* with clients so that our sessions together were more authentic and more meaningful.

With this new awareness, the natural step was to continue training and so my master's degree followed in integrative psychotherapy and counselling, which grounded me in the theoretical knowledge and experiential practice of relational level work. As is often the case, I was left with a desire for more and to further myself as a person and as a professional – drawing me to what I now consider to be the most illuminating way of working, existential psychotherapy, the focus of my doctoral training.

For me, being a therapist is not really a job at all, more a way of being. I rarely spend an hour with a client that resembles any other and every person I meet is wonderfully different. Every presenting problem is unique, and therefore the way I work with every client varies.

Being a therapist should be challenging for us, at times frustrate us, occasionally infuriate us and at times bring us joy. Ultimately, it will present to us the opportunity to experience the courage of people, and that for me is a privilege.

Sandra's Beginning

Twelve years ago my reason for becoming a therapist was rooted in unhappiness in my career and unrest in my life in general. As I completed my education degree, I had a dream of how my life would be, embarking on a career in secondary education for some thirteen years, eager to be as good as I could be, secretly desiring to be 'the best'. I worked hard teaching Physical Education, developing new GCSE and A level courses and being as involved within the hub of the school as I could. I thoroughly enjoyed all that I did and wanted more, or so I had myself believe. The school's head teacher showed great faith in me early on and I quickly gained promotion within the pastoral system and took to the challenge well, working ever harder to satisfy a driven part of me. I *had* to do well. I *had* to make a difference and keep busy, ever dodging a hidden anxiousness held within. Throughout all of this my body was riddled with trauma, frozen in time. At the age of 8 I had been a passenger in a car that aquaplaned and ploughed head on into a bus. This was raw unprocessed anguish, an experience yet to be fully and completely a memory. It was a story that I couldn't yet bear as a reality, so I just kept busy, never stopping to feel what was really held there.

Another promotion meant further 'busyness' that drove me to a stirring restlessness, of which I was now becoming mindful. I was beginning to feel harassed by my feelings and although unaware of my intentions at the time, I began to create a physical emptiness in order to sustain myself, woken only from this trance-like state by a forced period of sick leave, too thin and weak to function.

Four months later, I emerged back into my world and a year later I began therapy, which was my first experience of *talking* and *not talking* about myself, and during which I realised I wasn't thrilled by where I was or where I was going. Someone recommended hypnotherapy to help me move forward and as I entered into this, I began to be amazed by how differently I was starting to feel and how it opened me up to more of 'who' I was and 'how' I was.

So, I embarked on hypnotherapy training because it had worked for me, because I wanted to know more about it and, most importantly, to gain more insight into me. I was never that serious about becoming a therapist – far too much responsibility. Eleven years ago I would never have believed that I would be where I am now.

As I began training, a flame quietly and surprisingly ignited and flickered deep inside me as I began learning about me and learning skills and techniques that could help others. It wasn't until ten months into the course that it suddenly dawned on me that I might actually be able to *be* a therapist, finally accepting that secondary school teaching really wasn't for me. And so – I became a therapist. I finished my training and began to look at how this could all work, tentatively moving from full-time teaching to part-time work in an adolescent psychiatric unit, while building a part-time therapy practice.

I continued my hypnotherapy and psychotherapy training to advanced diploma level and it was here that I met existentialism, and with it, an uncontrollable urge to talk – to share myself and my thoughts – and I began to read with a passion not encountered before. I furthered my learning, specifically drawn to inner child therapy as this seemed to make healing sense to me. The concept of the 'inner child' within – holding limiting core beliefs and emotional blocks – introducing me to the unique process of being able to free the child within to greater emotional health and knowledge.

How was *I* as I gave therapy? In the beginning I would say that I 'delivered' therapy, unaware of the deeper lens I really was looking through. I had a 'big book' of suggestions and an armoury of techniques that meant if I matched the technique to the presenting problem and the client, it could work. I felt heavy with the responsibility of 'making people better' and making therapy work. I planned each individual client's session using a technique tailored to trying to solve the problem. My ears strained to hear every single word the client said, my forehead a permanent frown with the effort to assimilate all that was going on. I cringe at the tension I felt within and the lack of confidence that I suspect exuded from me. I battled with knowing that at this stage it was not yet possible to be a competent therapist. I knew it was only experience that would enable me to 'become' a therapist, and yet gaining experience meant working with people without this experience. It was a struggle!

In the early days, the main emphasis in my therapy was helping people feel understood and heard. Yet out of my awareness there was a yearning in me to be heard but, owing to circumstances in my past, this had not been possible. It was also personally meaningful to light up another's eyes, making someone feel good about themself, seeing a spark of self-respect and pride. Indeed, this was what first led me into teaching as I loved nothing more than to see students achieving and watching their faces glow with pleasure. This was *my* project in early life, to light up my family's eyes, which always seemed so sad and which became a desire that I carried deep within.

In becoming a therapist, these lost parts of me were being found and nurtured. It touched some things in me that were missing and that needed acknowledging and healing. This was my journey and once I became aware, I began working through these parts. What followed was a greater depth of me and hence my therapeutic practice. I became less of a 'being in the past' and more of a 'being of the now' with my clients and the dilemmas that they revealed.

So, in part, I was drawn to this work to heal and to grow. I was learning about myself as a human being and all that this entailed, and from this I found I was able to guide others to learn about themselves and how they could grow.

My extensive reading and desire to understand why I survived an un-survivable car crash led me to a three year master's degree and then on to doctoral training in existential psychotherapy and counselling, which culminated in a further process of maturation, a growing into myself and a recognition of 'being here' – a sense of actually being present in the world. Through attending theoretical modules, composing essays and personal therapy, I slowly delved into existence in general and my existence in particular; recognising many things about life, living and trauma; grieving for things that have been lost or never were. I have gradually become aware of my body and the trauma it has contained and remembered, understanding how I am and how I experience myself.

Twelve years on from the beginning of this journey, and many client hours later, I am still here and learning more all the time. What is different for me in therapy now is that I feel much freer when working, I am more 'me', more who I know as 'Sandra', and I am more comfortable with the uncertainty that sitting in front of a client brings – and it does! I do not know how the client will start their session, what they will say, what hypnotic intervention I will use (if any) or how the session will end. I *do* know that I work with the problems people are having with living, which starts but does not end with their presenting problem.

I remain, and continue choosing to be a therapist because working with people in this way is rich with life experiences and because I feel as if I am doing something valuable and worthwhile. Being a therapist changed my life and I hope it will, or has, changed yours.

Chapter 2

Cognitive Behavioural Hypnosis and NLP in Action

The Clenched Fist Auto Anchoring Technique (Tom)

> *Give a man a fish and he'll eat for a day;*
> *teach a man to fish and he'll eat for a lifetime.*
> Lao Tzu

The clenched fist technique, adapted from the work of Stein (1963), and later developed by Hammond (1990) offers us the power of 'anchoring' useful and positive thoughts and feelings within the client, so that they can access them in the future when they are most needed. The additional power of this technique is that we are not only teaching the client how to access these alternative experiences within a therapeutic session but also how they can 'trigger' off the desired experience on their own, in just about any scenario or situation they can think of, no matter who they are with or what they are doing. This is a powerful way for them to gain control of their behaviour.

Anchoring is explored extensively in neurolinguistic programming (NLP) (Bandler and Grinder 1979; Dilts 1983) and works from the understanding that when we experience an event, we 'store' it in our memory, including what we saw, heard, felt, thought, smelt and perhaps even tasted. In this we are referring to the five senses that we have in our experiencing of the world. Physical experiences can be powerfully anchored and stored in our bodies as a memory for many years. Try patting a grown man on the head and asking him how old he feels, or even pulling a woman's hair and asking the same. Often they are transported back through the years to school days where an adult would pat them on the head or girls would get their hair pulled by some secretly admiring young boy. We see this notion in the famous experiments of Ivan Pavlov, in which his dogs became conditioned to the sound of a bell that he anchored to feeding time, so that each time the dogs heard the bell they would start salivating. Here we see an example of how the body and mind remember and make links in experiences, which proves incredibly useful in therapy. This means we can 'teach' the body to react as we want it to and re-programme it to link with more desirable thoughts, helping us to experience certain situations as we would wish to.

> *You cannot shake hands with a clenched fist.*
> Indira Gandhi

Why the clenched fist? Often a self-anchoring method is used by putting the thumb and forefinger together to 'fire' powerful memories, thoughts and feelings stored away, collapsing the unwanted state. While this is useful, we feel that using a more natural behaviour increases the likelihood of a new strategy and response becoming programmed. Have you ever found yourself punching the air with delight or clenching your fists when experiencing a surge of powerful emotion? Tennis players regularly clench their fist once they have played a critical winning shot. By tapping into these natural behaviours we can bridge the gap between the client's current unwanted behaviour and their desired response.

The first part of this technique requires examination of the unwanted thoughts, feelings and behaviour. This is followed by an exploration into how the client wants to be, spending time eliciting as much of the sensory experience as possible. Someone simply saying they want to feel calm and relaxed is not enough; we want to know how that will feel. These new 'desired' reactions also need probing in terms of when the client has experienced them before; so that we have a reference point for them once we enter the hypnotic trance. For example, if it is confidence that is needed then we need to explore one or more situations in the client's life when they have felt confident, or if its calmness then we aim to understand when they have felt a powerful feeling of calm. If they can't recall any instances, then we need to find another desired reaction – one where they can imagine what it would be like. It is worth mentioning that clients can become quite upset at the realisation that, from their current perspective, they have never felt confident (or calm), so we need to be alert and aware for what feelings may come up. However, this happens rarely, as most people can find a snippet of the feeling that we can use.

> *When I dare to be powerful – to use my strength*
> *in the service of my vision, then it becomes less*
> *and less important whether I am afraid.*
> Audre Lorde

Having gathered our material about how the client is feeling and how they *want* to feel, we can move into inducing the hypnotic trance and teaching the anchoring method. Once trance is induced, we begin to guide our client to the experience they have been telling us about, when they felt ultra-confident (or whatever it is they want to feel). Once they have drifted back into that memory, then we can begin to heighten the sensory experience of it, fine tuning what they see, hear and feel within the memory, so that it becomes more powerful and distinct. Our tone of voice plays an important part in the excitement we create; as we excite the imagination, the memory can gain clarity. At this point we 'install' the clenched fist anchor by directing the client, as they experience their confidence becoming stronger, to clench their right fist (or left, depending on their dominant hand) tightly, suggesting to them as they do so that this will heighten the sensory experience and the visualisation will become more vivid and 'real'. As we talk them through this we continually refer to the anchor being created and finally suggest that the anchor has now been powerfully formed, ready for use at any point in the future.

At this stage we create another anchoring experience, this time a little different from the normal approach to anchoring. Simply creating a 'positive' anchor is often not enough as the unwanted feelings are just too strong to overcome. Also, in many cases, clients have experienced their anxiety-driven behaviour for many years and so the prospect of a simple action, such as putting their thumb and finger together or clenching a fist, seems almost too straightforward as a way of changing their experience. And so, as fitting with Milton Erickson's strategies, it becomes important to acknowledge their unwanted feelings, accept them as part of the client's reality and incorporate a way of working with them.

The next instruction for the client is to ask them to clear their mind and to allow themself to drift back into a previous time when they displayed their problematic behaviour. This may have been one of the experiences explored in the pre-hypnosis part of the session or another memory may come to mind. Whatever the client begins to recall, we need to know as soon as they have it in mind, so we ask them for a signal to let us know. Once they are there, we can begin to build an anchor in the other hand. We ask them now to clench the fist of the opposite hand from the one used to create the positive anchor, and as they do so, we suggest they are going to allow all of their unwanted thoughts and feelings to gather in that fist. As that happens, they are to 'lock' those thoughts and feelings into that fist tightly, letting us know when they have completed the task.

It is at this point that the client will often be feeling most uncomfortable. Our own level of confidence and expectation at this stage is vital as they will be looking to us now to give them a way out of this experience, which is what we are about to do. With the positive anchor created earlier we 'collapse' the unwanted anchor, along with those unwanted feelings locked into that fist, by now suggesting to the client that on your signal, you want them to clench their right hand (or dominant hand) into a fist and open their left hand, allowing all of those locked away and unwanted feelings to be released; and as they are released, their right hand triggers off the desired thoughts and feelings which were created earlier. The use of suggestion makes this experience more profound for the client and so you may suggest that as they do this they are transported back into that positive desired memory, experiencing the associated thoughts and feelings, filling their body and mind, while the unwanted feelings just dissolve away.

> *Only one thing registers on the subconscious mind: repetitive application – practice. What you practice is what you manifest.*
> Fay Weldon

Repeating this process two or three times helps the client to learn the technique, and together with your suggestions for them to practise this daily, we create a powerful way for them to 'do' something with the old unwanted state and thus its behaviour. When a client feels that they can concretely do something about how they feel, their motivation levels often rise, making a big difference to the outcome of therapy. After we bring the client out of hypnotic trance we explore the experience of the process and again encourage practice on a daily basis.

Let's hear the process in action.

Driving Test Anxiety

The Client's Presenting Problem

Jodie's mother telephoned asking me to help her 22-year-old daughter pass her driving test. I have worked with this problem on many occasions and I am pleased to help people achieve that memorable moment when a driving examiner says, 'Well done, you've passed!' In working with a client with an issue where there is only one clear desirable outcome, we are given a very definitive and measurable task.

Jodie had successfully passed her written theory exam, but had already made twelve attempts at her practical driving test and didn't want to attempt number thirteen only to fail again. From the outset I focused on the fact that the most important thing Jodie had initially told me was that she had indeed succeeded in one part of her test.

Choice of Technique

I felt that the ideal choice for the first session would be an anchoring technique. My client needed something to do to become an active participant in her new desired behaviour. It would give her something to take away and practice, while beginning to create a new perception of reality.

The Session

I felt quite anxious, and a little pressured, when Jodie's father turned up with his cheque book in hand and a look of expectation, asking 'How many sessions is this going to take?' It made me wonder momentarily which one of them was my client: Jodie's father, who had been paying for Jodie's driving lessons and now these sessions, or Jodie herself? After reassuring him that we would have a clearer picture at the end of the session and that he didn't need to stay with Jodie, he left, and Jodie and I began.

'How many sessions will it take?' is a question I am often asked and one that is incredibly difficult to answer. In my mind I had planned three to four sessions as this would give me time to teach her some relaxation methods, work with her current thoughts and beliefs and create a new resourceful state for her to 'step into' when she took her driving test.

Sandra: When I read Tom's experience of meeting Jodie and her father, I am reminded of how having someone else investing in a client's therapy (parent, partner, NHS) can be a little uncomfortable and disconcerting at times.

Here, Jodie's parents had paid for her driving lessons, her twelve previous tests and now her therapy. Tom reacts and rightly questions who he feels accountable to, his client or her father.

Occasionally, with clients, my mind drifts to how others would perceive my work. If the NHS or a parent/partner pays for a client's session, what are they expecting and how will they react if their expectations are not met? I must admit that (early on in my career) I have been drawn into focusing on what I think the fee-payer is hoping for from the therapy and not the outcome the person in the room necessarily wants.

Tom had a way of appreciating the father's involvement but then gently guides him out of the room, by taking charge and yet reassuring the father that his daughter is still in good hands. To have Jodie's father in the session would have been unhelpful and yet I wonder how many therapists instead would have been drawn into inviting them to stay out of social politeness.

In exploring the situation further with Jodie, it appeared that during her driving lessons no anxiety was aroused, whereas during the test she felt nervous, sweaty, would stutter when answering the examiner's questions and generally feel unwell, inevitably leading her to make mistakes.

After this exploration and some preparation with Jodie as to how events are anchored in our minds, and hence how we can make use of this, we continued.

> **Sandra:** I know that Tom enjoys a challenge and believes that he can succeed in such situations. There is something about an attitude to success here. He thrives off such work – phobias, smoking cessation, exams/tests – as they are all measurable in their outcome. Early on in practice, for some, this expectation can be *too* measurable and can challenge our belief in the process, fuel self-doubt and possibly infect the session, and so it is helpful to explore how you feel about such work and your own attitudes to success.

Tom: What is important to you about passing your test, Jodie?

It was important to find Jodie's reasons for passing her test as we are only truly motivated by our own driven desires.

Jodie: Well, I want to get out and be able to do my own thing. I'm fed up of being stuck at home. I need some independence!

Here, of course, I could have easily wandered off on a tangent. 'What does independence mean to you?' (chunking up to a higher meaning) or even 'How are you "stuck" when you are at home?' (chunking down – the detail of the experience of being stuck) being questions I could have easily followed. On this occasion however I asked myself the question, 'How would it help Jodie at this stage to answer these questions, potentially exposing deeper issues?' No, I thought, I simply have to 'teach' her how to adapt her 'faulty' thinking patterns into 'successful' ones and create a resourceful state in which she could take her next test. NLP beckoned.

> **Sandra:** Tom wonders about the wider meaning of his client's situation, such as Jodie's view of independence. Me? Well, I wonder about why she needed to fail twelve times and the possible pressure to please her parents.

I would have explored what parts of her test she failed to see if any patterns might emerge, drawing from this some limiting beliefs along with the triggers that were in operation, looking to change them logically, rationally and ultimately subconsciously through suggestion work – a much more detailed response.

Two different perspectives, both with successful outcomes, which show how our own past guides the therapy that we give, and what our point of focus becomes.

So, how did she then experience the actual driving test for real?

Tom: What do you notice happens for you in your test?

Here I look to reveal the undesired response in Jodie, rather than to hear her account of each failed attempt.

Jodie: That's easy, it's the noise. It's like I become aware of every car around me, just too much; the horns, the engines of the lorries, everything. I just can't think straight. And then I start to make mistakes.

Jodie had become primarily focused on what she heard (her auditory modality very much in action here). I find it important in these situations to work with the undesired responses using the modalities only, not the submodalities (the detail and content of the experience). When we do explore submodalities it is important to do so with the *desired* outcome only, as it will give it credence and power. A stronger thought tends to take precedence over a weaker one, and that is what we aim for in the creation of this resourceful state.

Sandra: Tom shares a fascinating view about exploring the past undesired response only via modalities and the desired behaviour, in detail, via the submodalities.

On reflection, breathing life into the past, and making it real, does indeed seem unhelpful, as it would excite the mind back into the unwanted feelings. Dwelling on failure is not helpful, especially twelve of them! In focusing on how different it is going to be in colour and fine detail, this would sound much more attractive and, for short-term therapy, is a more helpful approach.

Tom: Okay, Jodie, now tell me how you would like to experience this instead, ideally.

Jodie: I would love to just be able to shut out all the distractions and focus on the task in hand. Of course I want to be aware of any dangers, but just to stop listening to everything that's happening. I want my thoughts to be calm. That would be just great!

Tom: So tell me about a time when you felt that way. Perhaps an experience you had where you felt calm and your thoughts were quiet, a time where you felt completely focused on what you were doing.

Jodie: Well, there was the time when I passed my A levels. I was so relieved because I had worked so hard and had been so focused. It was a struggle, but I got what I wanted. I remember we all went out and celebrated.

Tom: So tell me about the feelings you experienced. What was it like?

Although this wasn't strictly an experience that was 'calm and focused', it was the one that Jodie's mind had presented. From here I could draw out the feelings that were related to her driving test, using this as the 'replacement experience' in the session. Here Jodie seemed to be linking the 'working hard at something and being focused' to gaining what she wanted (passing her A levels). I thought about how she must have performed well in her exams to achieve success in her A levels, which could also be incorporated in the experience she was wanting when taking her driving test.

Jodie: It was utter jubilation … excitement … I was so relieved. I had really focused on what I wanted and got it. It gave me such confidence.

Tom: Okay, Jodie, I want you to close your eyes and imagine you have just passed your exams again. How do you feel physically?

It was important to enhance the awareness of her kinaesthetic experience to fully associate her into this state, so that we could use this to create a powerful anchor.

Jodie: It's like a warm tingly feeling in my stomach.

From here we continue to access further feelings and thoughts to intensify the experience. I then take Jodie through a passive progressive induction utilising bodily relaxation as part of the strategy she would use before her actual test.

Tom: In a moment I want you to allow your subconscious mind to take you back to that time and that place when you felt really pleased with yourself because you had got what you really wanted, and you experienced that warm tingly feeling in your stomach. Just allow your subconscious mind to show you that time and place when you felt really pleased and proud about passing your exams and maybe even begin to experience the sense of confidence that you have, when you realise that all your focused hard work and sitting your exams successfully has meant that you have achieved what you wanted … And when your subconscious mind has given to your conscious mind that wonderful experience, then I want you to just nod your head to let me know.

Jodie nods her head.

Tom: That's wonderful, well done. Now I want your subconscious mind to just drift back into that experience … and begin to hear what you hear … see what you see … and feel what you feel, being aware of what's going through your mind. (Engaging all of the modalities – visual, auditory, kinaesthetic, auditory digital.)

Begin to become aware of the different sounds you hear around you, perhaps the sounds of people, or even the sound of silence … or you may become more aware of what you see in this place, the different objects around you, and the different colours … or you may become more aware of the sense you have in this place and the feelings you experience.

And as this happens, you continue to relax to an even deeper level of calm peaceful tranquillity and you can become aware of the feelings you are experiencing becoming even stronger and even more profound now.

And as this experience becomes even more real, I want you to close your dominant hand into a tight fist, and as you do that, begin to experience these feelings becoming even stronger. And as you clench that fist even tighter, feel the feelings of calm, focus and confidence become even stronger, enjoying that sense of achievement. (Linking her pleasure and sense of achievement to a deep sense of inner calm and peace.)

Tom: That's *right* (incorporating ambiguity), and as you continue to soak up this experience, and these wonderful feelings that just flow all the way through you, you know that just as you have experienced this once again, that at any time in the future, whenever you close your dominant (right) hand into a tight fist, just like this … you will feel once again these feelings of confidence, calm and focus, flowing back over you, feeling them from the inside out and outside in, with every part of you experiencing this sense of calm and every peace (ambiguity) of you feels wonderfully relaxed.

And now you can begin to experience a real sense of confidence in knowing that you have become even more in control of your feelings and thoughts. And now just allow that fist to relax and drift into an even calmer, more relaxed feeling as your mind becomes calm, quiet and clear.

At this stage we have created a positive anchor within the client that they can use at any point and in any situation where they find themselves wanting to bring back feelings of calm or confidence, or whatever the desired feelings are.

> **Sandra:** I may have drawn from several other memories and anchored them in the same way, 'stacking' them, bringing out specific memories of being calm, relaxed and focused.
>
> For me, this creates a powerful multi-layered experience to fire off and collapse any anxieties, but Tom did this using just one memory. He told me he sensed it was enough, as when she described the experience it resonated within him and was powerful enough not to need any further strengthening. This is a simple technique that necessitates a sense of simplicity throughout, which is what we see here.

Tom: Now, very soon, you are going to be able to cancel out any of those anxious feelings and replace them with feelings of confidence and calm (or the desired feelings). So … I would like you now, Jodie, to begin to remember that time in the past where you were about to take your driving test with those unwanted feelings of anxiety. And when you're feeling again *some* of those unwanted feelings … then just let me know. (I wait until Jodie nods.)

Now I want you to begin to imagine all of those unwanted thoughts and feelings beginning to flow towards your shoulder and flow down, through your arm, your forearm, down into your (left or non-dominant) fist as you clench that now. Move all of those unwanted feelings into your (left) fist. And when it feels as if all of them are stored up in that (left) fist, then you can just nod your head again to let me know. (She nods.)

Excellent. Now you can begin to know … just how you can cancel those feelings out, instantly and immediately, and begin to feel just what you want to feel instead. So, in a moment … you can begin to see just how powerful your ability is to take control … and it works just like this.

I want you now to squeeze that dominant (right) hand into a tight fist, and as you do so, allow that left hand to relax. That's right, just move your fingers around on your left fist, allowing all those unwanted feelings to just flow out of your hand and away.

And as you squeeze your right hand and open your left, feel yourself transported back into that wonderful feeling of confidence and calm and enjoy that wonderful experience again, with your fist tightly closed and just enjoying taking several deep relaxing breaths and then, just find yourself relaxing deeply.

Because from this moment forward, whenever you want to take control of how you feel and what you think, all you need to do is close your left hand into a fist, allow all of those unwanted feelings to flow and funnel down into that fist, and when it feels as though you have locked them all up there then you can cancel them out, instantly and immediately, by clenching your right hand and opening your left.

At this stage I take Jodie through this process another two or three times to instil and condition the process deep within her subconscious mind.

And in a few moments it will be time for you to return to full awareness, bringing back with you this wonderful new ability of yours to take control in whatever situation you find yourself, no matter where you are or what you are doing, and Jodie, especially when you are on your driving test, you can take control and hear yourself quietly reminding yourself that *you* are in charge and you are in control …

And then I bring Jodie out of hypnosis.

> **Sandra:** The whole session has focused on success; the ability of the client to pass her A level exams and also the ability she has to take control of her thoughts and feelings. The hypnotic intervention accesses a deep faith in the client and the power of her subconscious mind. Tom suggests that, as she immerses into her memory of passing her A levels, she will feel even deeper levels of calm and peace, and he continues building success upon success. I imagine that each word was said with passion, belief and faith, all helping to create a new 'truth' for Jodie.

As Jodie opened her eyes a tear rolled down her cheek and we sat in silence. If I have learnt anything over the years, it is about the power of silence. In seeing Jodie's tears I could easily have moved into wanting to find out what they were for. I had my ideas – the tears accompanying a sense of relief and a realisation for Jodie that she now had a way forward and a strategy for success.

I sat and waited for Jodie to look up at me, whereupon she smiled. Clients, as they engage in the intricate processes of their sessions, become absorbed in themselves and on occasions we cease to exist for them, becoming just a voice in the distance. As Jodie looked up at me, we began to engage.

'How are you?' I said, offering her an opportunity to connect with me. She described how powerful it felt for her to isolate her thoughts and feelings and to feel that she now had something to work with and a way to take control.

> **Sandra:** I was moved by Tom's genuineness; he offered Jodie something simple and yet complex, just 'being there' for her. He doesn't need to know if the technique has worked (as he assumes and knows that it has), why she is tearful or what she will do now. Tom knows that their work is meaningful and conveys this to her in his silence.

The Processing of the Session

Jodie seemed to embrace this session, enthusing about her experience and how she would practise it further. I felt passionate about our work as this meant so much to her – desperately wanting to pass her driving test and gain her independence.

At the end of the session my thoughts once again turned to her parents, because when Jodie's father came to pick her up, exactly one hour later, her smile seemed to melt him to a degree that filled me with warmth. When I asked her about the arrangements for our next session, she looked at her father and he told her that he would fit in with whatever she needed. A smile can tell a thousand words, I thought.

What Happened Next?

In the following session, a week later, we worked on Jodie's concerns using another anchoring method and additionally I taught her self-hypnosis to give her some relaxation techniques that she could use when she needed them. She had been practising the clenched fist technique every day, as she had promised herself. Her enthusiasm was infectious!

To build on her incredibly positive attitude, I carried out a further two sessions using the SWISH technique (see page 40) and what is known in NLP as the changing memories exercise, which alters the submodality perception of the stored memory and thus changes the memory. Both approaches were designed to give her a different perspective on her past experiences of her driving test and create a new 'state' from which to take her next test.

One week after the sessions had finished, Jodie phoned me. I was excited and anxious to hear how her driving test had gone. My heart began pounding, I started sweating – indeed I started to experience all of the symptoms she originally described! She screamed, 'I passed, I passed, I passed! … Thank you, thank you so much!'

What did I say? 'I am very proud. Well done and … where are you driving today?' The remainder of the call involved Jodie telling me how the test went and her father saying how he was so proud of his daughter and was so thankful for what I had done. Following this her sister came on the phone and asked me if I could help her with her boyfriend's depression. And there lay a whole new story.

Sandra: Subsequent sessions covered a range of effective NLP/cognitive techniques that really made a difference, altering the client's present position and building from past experiences into future expectations and possibilities.

Tom had faith in Jodie and believed she would pass her driving test and was looking forward to enjoying her success. This is vital to maximise the experience for the client. Thirteen *was* lucky for her and I'm moved to wondering just what else she will achieve in her life now.

The Theatre Screen Technique (Sandra)

> *Time is a sort of river of passing events, and*
> *strong is its current; no sooner is a thing brought*
> *to sight than it is swept by and another takes*
> *its place, and this too will be swept away.*
> Marcus Aurelius Antoninus

The theatre screen technique is derived from the original work of the NLP master and co-creator himself, Richard Bandler. Originally described as the V/K (visual/kinaesthetic) dissociation technique, this method allows us to re-orient the client into a new experience through the 'rewinding' of their problem scenario, extracting the old emotional reactions (of fear, anxiety, dread) and leaving them with simply the factual details of the experience, devoid of the problematic feelings. The approach has also been described as the 'rewind technique' by Joe Griffin and Ivan Tyrrell of the Human Givens Institute (see also Muss 1991).

So often in therapy we are asked to help our clients feel 'better', yet when we delve into what better actually means for them, we are faced with a look of surprise and sometimes confusion. For many, better simply means 'not the way I'm feeling'. This technique allows us to create a powerful state of *indifference*, which more often than not fits well when working with phobias or if the client's desire is simply to be rid of their current unwanted feelings.

> *Everything is pathology, except for indifference.*
> Emile M. Cioran

Once we have induced the hypnotic trance, the client is invited to imagine themself at the entrance doors of a theatre or cinema. We guide them to push the doors open and walk down to the front row. At this point we are mindful that most people who walk into a theatre or cinema will encounter others already sitting waiting and excited for the show to begin, and so the client is told that they are the only person present in the theatre/cinema; alone, but totally safe, secure and comfortable. They are then guided to the centre of the front row of seats and invited to sit down.

> *Life does not proceed by the association and addition*
> *of elements, but by dissociation and division.*
> Henri Bergson

Usually we would continue by asking our client to look up and see their 'problem' scenario being projected onto the screen in front of them. However, as this method is so often used with phobias, or equally powerful anxiety-provoking situations, it can sometimes be useful to incorporate the use of a dissociative (or distancing) strategy, so as to offer the client a safe way of accessing the unwanted experience, without the attached fear or panic. More often than not our client is terrified that they will have to confront and experience these feelings, and indeed many would run a mile at this thought. Instead we can allow them to see their 'fear' on the screen in front of them, but from a third-person perspective: a view of viewing themselves watching the screen.

To do this we next guide our client to imagine sitting down in their seat, in the middle of the front row, and then imagining gently drifting up out of themselves, their body staying in the seat, yet them floating up and backwards to a seat in the back row, or the next tier up in the theatre. In doing this we create the separation of the client's 'self' and their 'anxiety self', allowing us at any time during the technique (if re-association occurs) to suggest that they can float into their 'dissociated self' (we use the phrase 'separated self' to keep our language simple) at the back and just observe themselves watching the screen, and allowing the technique to continue.

We then ask the client to see the projected image of their problem or anxiety-provoking scenario on the screen in front of them. We guide them to become aware of what they see, hear and feel about the image on the screen, which is frozen in that scenario, as if the movie is about to play but has been paused, giving the viewer time to become aware of its content.

Next, we suggest that the movie is now going to play and we ask them to describe what is happening in detail on the screen. As they tell us, we can repeat their words to follow them and bring more clarity to the film, and we suggest to them that when the movie of this problem scenario comes to the end, that they are to then pause it and just see the image on the screen in front of them.

When they have talked us through the movie and paused it at the end, we can begin to 'extract' the emotion by changing the film – thus re-programming the way it is stored away. So we now ask them to play the movie backwards, as if they were rewinding the action, seeing it playing in reverse, the images moving backwards, until they reach the beginning, at which point the client is to pause it again.

Then we ask them to play the film forwards again, and describe to us what they see, until they again reach the end. We listen and make note of any changes to the content of the movie as they describe it. When they reach the end, again we guide them to play it in reverse, this time rewinding it faster than the first time, per-haps at double the speed. Once they have rewound to the begin-ning, the client is to pause it as before, and we then guide them to describe the film as it plays *again* through to the end, where it is again paused. As the client does this we make further note of how the movie is described as it may be in this description that we hear the emotion being omitted from the story as the experience is 're-coded' in the brain.

Often the client is encouraged through a further playing and rewinding of the movie, each time the speed getting faster. This is done three or four times, and we listen for the story to become devoid of emotion, until the client tells you what sounds like a purely *factual* description of what they are watching.

> *The degree of one's emotions varies inversely with one's knowledge of the facts.*
> Bertrand Russell

At this point the client is asked to rewind the film once more, then to pause it on the screen. To check that the client has fully mentally re-programmed the experience, they are then asked to imagine climbing into the movie on the screen (associating them into the experience) and to one last time play the movie, with them in it, from the beginning to the end. When they reach the end they rewind it once more to the beginning, when they then climb out of the screen, positioning themself back in their seat in the front row. Providing this proves successful, and the client has re-encoded or re-processed the experience, then we are ready to bring the technique to an end, which we do simply by suggesting to the client to blank out the screen (if we suggested to them to float up to the back row, then now they float back into themself) and begin walking back to the theatre doors that they entered earlier. When they reach the doors they can walk on through and allow their eyes to open.

We have found this technique creates amazingly powerful changes in the client's perception of their problem scenario very quickly, whether a phobia has been affecting the client's life for five months or fifty years.

So let us see how we integrate the theatre screen technique into our work.

Agoraphobia

The Client's Presenting Problem

Jill's husband originally phoned wanting help with his wife's fear of going out as she could no longer drive on her own or venture outside without becoming extremely anxious or panicky.

I do not usually meet a client prior to the first therapy session; however, I found myself setting up a brief twenty minute get-together with Jill so she could explain a little about what she was experiencing. The fact that her husband had made the initial contact encouraged me to meet Jill; I was struck by the fact that someone else had spoken with me about my client which made me feel uncomfortable. I said nothing of this at the start of our twenty-minute meeting (which ended up being forty minutes), knowing that things would likely unfold in the ensuing therapeutic relationship. Jill looked very young for her 39 years, unsure and scared, and struggling to verbalise how she was feeling, which gave me a little more insight into why her husband had rung me to explain the situation.

I focused my attention on Jill as much as possible to find out what it was like being her: lacking in confidence, having difficulties being outside her home, going into shops and driving alone. During our discussion, I encouraged her to consider what she would like to work on initially and she decided this was 'being able to go out into town'. My opening session aims to give the client control over their own destiny, which I consider an important part of the early stages of therapy, as nobody knows the individual and their problem better than they do. I hold a 'knowingness' that there are hidden depths and strengths in the client and meanings that need to be found, which can only come from their own curious self-exploration and empowerment.

Jill had reached a point in her life where things were closing in around her. She was stuck in the office at work and when her husband was not around she was pretty much housebound at home, and she was beginning to feel like a burden to her family. She was scared, confused and tired of how she felt all the time. Thankfully, for Jill, my practice was within bearable walking distance from her home, so she was able to make the journey to our sessions alone, which was indeed the first big challenge she set herself.

Tom: The first thing that struck me was the start of this therapy process and how from the very first phone call the ownership of Jill's problem appeared fragmented. I can see why Sandra offered the get-together session to meet Jill for herself, which possibly cemented a much needed transparency in the relationship between them from the outset, but I would not have done this. I can see that this was virtually a full session of therapy and I wonder why Sandra didn't book the first session and allow the husband to come along should they deem it to be helpful. Therapy clearly started from this exposure anyway.

There was a sense that Jill needed to begin to take charge, and here the work begins as Sandra gets her to choose what she would like to work on first. A therapist needs to have confidence in their client's ability and their wisdom, while also standing resolute in a place of 'unknowingness' to help them achieve this.

Clients suffering from agoraphobia have the challenge of coping with the fear of panicking as well as the original fear that led them to their first panic attack. Many clients are caught up in a cycle of being ultra-vigilant with their internal physical responses, so any small bodily change is seen as an emergency – feeling they may faint, make a fool of themselves or even something worse. The root of the problem is often lost once they are in the cycle of 'the fear of fear'. Clients often describe themselves as desperate and frustrated because it all seems illogical and irrational to them, yet they can't seem to stop it.

Initially I look to teach my client strategies that will help in the event of a possible panic attack, while at the same time beginning to work with the deeper roots of the problem. In their descriptions they can get closer to gaining a more genuine understanding, and thus empathy with themselves. From here the client often recognises patterns and becomes curious for further self-knowledge, beginning to engage in the process and naturally getting closer to making the changes they desire. Stopping the panic attacks can be relatively easy; it is looking beyond the surface that requires the real skill of the therapist.

Some years previously Jill had suffered from panic attacks, indicating to me that they were meaningful, and thus were now alerting her to something that needed attention. Later on in Jill's therapy we meet her anxiety about her place in life – and the dilemmas she held around work, starting a family or in fact ending her relationship – which linked with her fear of not being good enough, not knowing herself and of life just passing her by.

Choosing the Technique

As you may have gathered the initial meeting virtually became the first session, and so in our second session we explored what her lack of confidence felt like, along with the experience of her panic attacks, and together we gained an outline of her thoughts, feelings (emotional and physical) and behaviours.

She described feeling anxious, her heart racing, being unable to breathe and feeling sick, tearful and panicky. Her worries and thoughts were focused on people looking at her and she was convinced that something was going to happen that would leave her looking ridiculous. This left her desperate to escape the situation and avoid it in the future at all costs. As she described this experience I began to hear that indeed all of her worry was centred entirely on having a panic attack.

I spent time in therapy building a thorough picture of how she would like to be, so she knew what she was aiming for and what it would be like when she reached it (future pacing). I aimed to excite her mind so it could begin to search for snippets of resourceful feelings from the past and present – and imagine it as a reality in the future where they could be anchored.

In this, our third session, I thought I might use the theatre screen technique, focusing on the 'anxiety movie' of going out in public and changing it to a film of indifference. My aim was that she would be able to go out in public, and from this significant change a sense of 'What else can I do?' would emerge.

I also decided to incorporate the miracle day scenario (imagining the symptoms no longer exist – see Glossary of Terms), to enable Jill to creatively experience her most resourceful self – shaping a new referential state so she could begin to realise and reach out towards it in the future.

Tom: Sandra begins by focusing not just on what the client considers the 'problem' feelings, but also how the client 'wants' to be. I remember one of the most powerful sessions of therapy I ever had with a client was when I asked them, at the start of their first session, 'What would it be like to leave here today as if your problem never existed?' We spent three sessions working with the fear of that very possibility! So it is vital that we focus on how our clients want to be, along with their expectations of that reality, as we often don't know their position in relation to change.

The Session

Sandra: How has the week been?

Jill: Great, I felt really good after I left here last week. I was really positive and went straight out for a walk and even wandered around the supermarket. It's been a good week actually. I even went out during a lunchtime. I was a little anxious but I was able to do it. I told myself that I needed to do it and there was nothing to be afraid of!

Sandra: Tell me a little more about what it was like going out into town.

I'm staying with her story to gain a greater description of the sequence of events in detail, deconstructing further what is being held within. So far, from previous sessions, I only have a description of 'When I go out I feel anxious – I panic.'

Jill: Well, I sat in the office and decided that I was going out. I told myself that I could do it and that I was being silly. I had one job to do and I could do it. I still felt anxious though, but at lunchtime I got up and went out to the shop and then came back.

It would be all too easy to give praise and encouragement here, but we are looking at helping her move her thinking forward, so I refrain.

Sandra: When you became anxious, what was it like?

Jill: It felt like I couldn't breathe and my heart raced.

Sandra: (I repeat her words so she hears them again and add) … What were you thinking at this time?

I remained silent as she seemed to search her thoughts. Time is needed for the client to recapture, and in some respects open up to, the thoughts attached to her experience; her 'perception' of the feelings and the interpretation of the situation is often a problem.

Jill: I got muddled and scared. I felt alone and worried, then frustrated and angry with myself (the judgement).

The client still has not described how she thinks in this place, although we have insight into something important here in that she 'felt' alone.

Sandra: And when you felt muddled, scared and alone, feeling like you couldn't breathe, what were you thinking? (I reword my question.)

Jill: I am going to fall … There is no one there that I know … I can't get back to work … and I can't explain myself.

Here we begin to gain a good description of her thoughts.

Tom: In the initial part of the session, the client begins to describe her experience with Sandra's questions taking her from her feelings to her thoughts. It is in this dialogue, 'I am going to fall … There is no one there that I know … I can't get back to work … and can't explain myself,' that we see a great deal of information coming from the client. I felt my own mind racing into what I would have said, and found myself repeating Jill word for word, slowing the pace down and taking each statement carefully on its own, delving deeper into her felt experience and bringing it into the room. Sandra chooses one of Jill's statements about being alone and explores this in depth.

Sandra: I am hearing that being quite alone is significant.

I was drawn to this statement. She paused and flushed slightly.

Jill: Yes, it's like that in the car as well. I can drive anywhere and go out as long as I'm not on my own. I just feel panicky when I'm alone.

Sandra: So what does being alone mean to you?

I hoped this might uncover the deeper essence of Jill's experiencing of herself.

> **Tom:** 'What does being alone mean to you?' At first sight this seems like a simple intervention but it takes Jill's story into something much more profound – into that of 'meaning'. Here I see Sandra's existential nature at work, and what comes of this is a new richness in Jill's responses – she becomes more present in the session and more animated and descriptive.

Jill: It's something that didn't really bother me before. I lived on my own for a few years and went out and to work with no problems. But now I'm scared of being alone in case I panic. I feel like I am totally alone then. Everyone is moving around me so fast and I'm confused and light headed. It's like I won't be able to manage or I'll get left behind.

My mind drifts to being left behind in life, not being able to manage the pace of life, with time passing by. At this point in the session my head is spinning with questions and I wonder if this is similar to how it is for Jill when she becomes anxious and panicky.

Sandra: I feel quite overwhelmed and dizzy as I imagine being 'you' in town. It seems a very physical experience where you're acutely aware of what is happening *to* you.

Jill: That's exactly how it is. I'm afraid that I'm going to have a panic attack, so I monitor how anxious I'm feeling and then I start to analyse it and get frustrated with myself and then I wonder why I feel this way. It's like this all the time, Sandra.

> **Tom:** In getting this response, Sandra clearly begins to resonate with Jill's experience and feels what it is like in Jill's world and reflects this perfectly. From here Jill describes how she 'does this all the time'. *All* the time? I question, as my linguistic love affair of generalisations descends upon me!

Sandra: Okay, how about we explore in hypnosis how your mind is holding a movie of the relationship between going out and panicking?

As Jill agrees we continue. A passive progressive relaxation induction is used (as her experience is a very physical one), with suggestions about the benefits of relaxation, and then I guide Jill into the cinema asking her to project on the screen an image of the fear she has of 'going out' and then to play the movie of it from start to finish, letting me know when she has finished. She described a trip to town feeling anxious and panicky. I ask her to rewind the film to the beginning and then play it forward changing it to black and white, and to then play it backwards rewinding it again from end to beginning, and to do this twice more. I then tell her to play the film forwards describing to me what is happening. She tells me that the movie is 'okay' now, describing walking through town, looking in shops.

I then ask Jill to step into the movie and run it again, asking her how she is experiencing other people – what speed they are going and whether this matches the speed she is going (it does). I ask her also what shops she is looking in and how that feels. She describes a shoe shop, a pair of red shoes and how relaxed she feels. And as she sounds surprised at this, I suggest further how relaxed she is becoming and encourage her to notice what is around her, to externalise her experience, as previously there was only her internally focused reality. The film ends with her needing to go back to work.

I ask her then if there is anything else she notices about the movie, or perhaps anything she would like to change which would make the experience more relaxing and enjoyable. Jill tells me that she keeps looking at her watch and here I notice time coming into the session again. So we go through the film once more, this time without the watch on. I continue to suggest calmness and relaxation and inner confidence.

Jill tells me that she is happy with the movie and so I ask her to play it twice more and then step out of the screen into her seat in the front row, and then to leave the cinema.

> **Tom:** Sandra moves through the session, reminding me just how versatile this technique can be. When 'time' starts to creep into the session, Sandra simply suggests that Jill has no watch on! With this kind of creativity, whatever your client presents, you can work with.

From here I ask her to imagine herself tucked up in bed, imagining that during the night a miracle has occurred and she is just the way she would like to be, with all the resources she could ever want or need. I ask her that in this miracle day, when she opens her eyes in the morning, to be aware of the first thing that tells her this miracle has happened and to tell me what it is. She says she feels happy and bright. I ask her how this is and she describes it as feeling sunny, calm and settled. I then ask her to continue her day and notice how being happy, calm, settled and bright is – noticing how it is being 'her' with these feelings. I then suggest that her conscious and subconscious mind work together from this moment forwards, processing and experiencing all the feelings of calmness, inner confidence and balance, feeling sunny, calm and settled.

Sandra: How was that?

Jill: That was really good! I was surprised about looking at my watch … It felt like I was under the pressure of time to get back to work.

Sandra: Time and the pressure of time are meaningful?

Jill: Yeah … I don't like to be late for anything and I definitely like order. I'm quite a routine person and I like to get things done and not waste time.

Sandra: Time and the pressure of time seem significant in your life and I'm wondering perhaps if we can come back to this in the next session, as we are nearing the end of our time today. Before we finish, just imagine going into town next week: what happens as you do? (This future pacing is important as it checks out what changes have occurred in the movie of 'going into town' and if we need to tweek the reconstruction any more.)

Jill ponders a while.

Jill: Yes, it seems more possible. I feel more positive about it.

Sandra: That's great and I'm looking forward to hearing how different this is all going to be for you next week.

The Processing of the Session

I felt uncomfortable at the beginning of the session as I struggled to connect with Jill, finding myself engaging only in her words. Time seemed to go very slowly as Jill found it hard to explain how she was feeling and gave short responses to my questions and reflections. It felt a bit like verbal tennis, where I was continually serving an ace, and I wondered if this was how she found being with other people – always having to answer questions and explain herself. It didn't seem easy for her and I felt a little awkward and self-conscious as I shared in her description of how it was.

She came across – in her manner, choice of words, tone of voice and appearance – as much younger than her years, which I had noticed in our initial discussion, and yet I began to see a maturity, a grit and determination.

However, I couldn't imagine her in her job as a PA or doing the domestic chores she described in the first session. Indeed I wasn't sure 'what' I could imagine her doing in fact, which I was curious about.

Tom: The session moves out of the hypnotic element quickly and for me a level of detachment occurs. 'How was that?' Sandra asks. 'That was really good,' Jill responds. Is Sandra affected by the client or influenced in some way by her own journey?

Sandra asks Jill how the work they have done in the session will impact on her week. Personally I would have waited, not wanting to 'test' the work before the client has had time to integrate it into themself.

There is a belief however that something has and will happen. She ends the session in true hypnotherapeutic style as she 'wonders' at how being in town will be. Milton Erickson would have been proud of this suggestion. It feels true, apt, genuinely felt and fitting with the client's experience.

What Happened Next?

Jill came back the following week pleased with herself. She had been out into town every day that week and indeed never lost the ability to do so from this session onwards. She was surprised at how 'normal' it felt and was keen to now start working on being able to drive on her own. Our future sessions explored her pressured work – her boss eroding her confidence leaving her frustrated, enraged and doubting herself. She really vented her feelings and suggested that the reactions she had in the car seemed linked to her experiences at work.

Following this session we used anchoring via the clenched fist technique to help boost her confidence in times of anger and frustration at work and also explored the strategy she used for driving, looking to change the moment of anxiety via the SWISH technique (see below). This got her back into the car driving, with the proviso being that she didn't drive to work (for now) so that her mind wasn't able to link work with driving. I think she got the point about anchored experiences well.

Our time together came to an end around six months later during which time we had explored many aspects of her life leading her to a greater understanding of her thoughts, feelings and responses. Having made many changes she felt in charge and able to listen and respond to herself much more effectively than when we first met.

The SWISH Technique (Sandra)

> *NLP is a methodology that leaves*
> *behind a trail of techniques.*
> Richard Bandler

One of the many techniques included in the application of NLP is called SWISH (Bandler 1985), so named because we '*swissshh*' away un-useful thoughts and feelings and replace them with more resourceful ones. The SWISH technique is a dynamic method for helping clients to create a new response from what would have been a trigger for an old unwanted behaviour, thus forming a powerful link to a better reality.

In its purest form, SWISH is used as a visual method of changing our perception of a problem scenario. However, we can also incorporate other modalities into the technique, such as sound (saying the word 'swish') or by getting a feel of the change, to appeal to the kinaesthetic modality.

The easiest way to form a mental picture of the SWISH process is to think of a mirror on a dressing table or bedroom wall. Many people view the mirror in their bedroom as more personal than those in other rooms of their home, and therefore imagining this mirror often helps to create meaning for the client and can conjure up the image of a photograph tucked in the corner of a fond old memory, significant person or themselves as they once were.

> *Success is the progressive realization*
> *of a worthy goal or ideal.*
> Earl Nightingale

Imagine now that you change the picture tucked in the corner into an image of 'you' having created the perfect behavioural response to the problem situation. To do this you need to imagine just how you would like to think, feel, react and 'be' once the desired response has become a reality. Occasionally we have both worked with clients who simply could not visualise themselves as they wanted to be. If my client says to me that they can't see themselves, I ask them to 'pretend' and to take a snapshot of it, and put it in place of the picture in the corner. This change in wording more often than not takes away the concept of visualising and allows them to create the image in their own unique way. However, from a visual perspective, I make sure that they see this image in the brightest, most colourful and vibrant way they can. I remember as a child being mesmerised watching *The Wizard of Oz*, as after five or so minutes the movie changes from black and white to the most beautiful Technicolor I had ever seen at the time. It became enthralling, exciting and full of life, and this is what we want our clients to create.

So we have the mirror and the desired image tucked in the corner. Our next step is to bring the problematic image or scenario into the equation. I have always found that in the session, the client believes the problem still exists, and so the mirror acts as the perfect way to bring their problem scenario into the process. The client is invited to bring the image of them with the problem situation into the mirror, creating the image they want to replace, noticing a trigger submodality that would normally create the undesired response. You can ask them to make this a black-and-white image, purely to detract from the visual stimulus that a colour image may give them, and thus reducing the emotional content. However, for some, a black-and-white image may hold a sense of nostalgia or create a specific ambience; if in doubt ask the person who knows the most about this – your client.

We now have our 'working' images for the SWISH process to begin. Our next step is to begin changing the images so that the desired one becomes the expected scenario. There are many variations on how to do this. My own preferred style is simply to prepare the client for what they are to do next. I have found that most clients are positively encouraged by your confidence in the procedural steps of the method you are using, so exude plenty of it! This creates a sense that something *is* going to happen, which presupposes movement before the process has even started. Your own belief in this process is key to a successful outcome.

> *Motion creates emotion.*
> Anthony Robbins

I tell my client that in this unfolding process, as they begin to swap the pictures over, the colour image of them as they want to be will fill the mirror, and the picture of them with their current unwanted behaviour will shrink down into the corner of the mirror.

I then guide them to reverse the process, so that the colour picture shrinks down again into the corner and the black-and-white picture fills the mirror. Here we are simply directing the swapping over of the pictures and then swapping them back again, so our client knows what they are going to be doing as we proceed.

Now they know what the first part of this process entails we can continue. With the colour picture again filling the mirror and the black-and-white picture shrinking down to the corner, I begin to add some powerful suggestions into the scene. I ask my client to repeat the process and this time, as they swap the pictures over, to hear in their mind a 'swishing' sound, which adds an auditory experience to the process. I wait a few moments and ask them to feel, hear and see what this is like, and then swap and SWISH the images back once again, the black-and-white picture filling the mirror and the colour one shrinking to the corner.

The next step is when we capitalise on the power of suggestion, and for me this is where SWISH becomes most potent. I ask my client to continue this process, adding that from now on, each time they swap and SWISH the images back and forth, that the black-and-white image (their unwanted behaviour) begins to fade away and becomes faint and distant, and that each time they repeat this process the black-and-white image continues to fade more and more. From here I encourage them through the process a further three or four times, following which I suggest that 'very soon, in a moment, before they know', the black-and-white image will have faded away completely, and all that will be left in the mirror is the image of them as they want to be, with the desired thoughts, feelings and behaviour there in the mirror, in full Technicolor. I ask them to nod their head when that image is all they can see.

> *The greatest happiness is to transform*
> *one's feelings into action.*
> Madame de Stael

For me, the most exciting part of this technique is the incorporation of the desired outcome as a reality; as an *embodied* reality. This is what creates action for the client – the very 'real' (albeit imagined) experience of what they have created.

When the client has indicated that they are left with the colour image of them in the mirror, I ask them to *stretch* themselves into the mirror, into that image, to become it, to try it on for size and to immerse themselves into just what it feels like in mind and body to be that 'them', experiencing the reality they have always wanted. I invite them to imagine strolling around and getting in touch with the power that they feel in what they have created. After a few minutes of experiencing this I then suggest to them that they can then stretch back *out* of the mirror, bringing all they have created back with them, and follow on with various suggestions as to how their life is now going to be within this new vision of themself.

The most profound reactions often come at this stage, with clients who never imagined things could be different experiencing the changes that have taken place. From here I guide them out of hypnosis into an exploration of the experience and its meaning for them now and in the future.

SWISH can appear a deceptively simple technique, yet I am always astounded at just how powerful it can be. As said previously, a number of variations of this technique can be used. We can 'push' the unwanted image out into the distance, and then bring it in as close as possible, incorporating some spatial distortion, or as shown above, we can immerse the client 'into' the desired image, embodying the changes that we have created.

So, let's see how this works in a session.

Relaxation and Self-Hypnosis

The Client's Presenting Problem

Mark (aged 30) contacted me asking for help with relaxation and to learn some self-hypnosis techniques. He wanted to feel more emotionally balanced and think more positively instead of his tendency to over-analyse and worry. When we initially met, he told me of his multiple sclerosis (MS) diagnosis some six years ago. He described how, during the winter, he experienced MS flare-ups which caused him to have double vision and to be physically unbalanced. His medication was also producing harsh side effects: he was suffering quite badly from low energy and feelings of numbness in his legs, which he was struggling with as he used to enjoy regular exercise, archery and keeping fit.

Generally his symptoms were not visible to others and for most of the time he was able to carry on with his life uninterrupted. Mark described himself as having a 'short fuse', with small things beginning to irritate him and dragging him into a negative mindset at home and at work. He was feeling very tired all of the time and was looking for a general boost of energy, both physically and psychologically.

This was my first experience of working with someone with MS. As with all medical diagnoses, there was a need to check carefully for contraindications in using hypnosis. I took a detailed history about his situation, the medication and its side effects, and the attacks he described. Mark was very knowledgeable about his condition and had clearly done a great deal of research into how to slow down the process of MS and how to help himself stay as healthy as he could. His specialists were regularly monitoring how his medication was affecting him and felt hypnotherapy might be helpful to him.

I wondered about the onset of such a debilitating condition so early on in Mark's life. I remembered one of my own family members being diagnosed with Parkinson's disease and then watching the slow and steady deterioration of their body into malfunction and ultimate extinction, and how difficult this was to be a part of, let alone experience personally. As these thoughts and images came into my mind I felt sad for this young, motivated family man, but recognised that I needed to put this to one side. After all, in his initial phone call he did not say, 'Hi, I am looking for sympathy. Can hypnosis help?' He wanted help in his present way of being and his responses to the world. This may include an exploration of being diagnosed with MS and about his thoughts and feelings about his future, or it may not.

In our first session I confirmed that he had indeed been checked out recently by his specialists regarding his lethargy and the numbness in his legs, as I did not want our work to hide something that signified the need for medical intervention. As I explored the bigger picture of his worries, negative thinking and over-analysing, he revealed a deep need to provide for his family and a concern that this might not always be possible. He also shared an innate fear of living with MS and the impact this would have on his future.

As Mark described his story I began to build a clear picture of his life now and how he would like it to be. This first session ended with me teaching him some relaxation techniques, and how to access a place of peace and serenity which included positive suggestions of well-being. He absolutely loved the experience and said it had already really helped him.

Choosing the Technique

For our second session we planned to work specifically on what Mark had described as his 'negative head'. His description of this specific state, which he wanted to change to a more resourceful one, together with Mark's very visual experience of the world brought SWISH to mind as being the first technique to teach him.

I used SWISH in the following way. We focus on the creation of two pictures. The first image (1) reflects the moment just before the person enters into the undesired state/behaviour, and the second image (2) reflects how they would be if they didn't experience this undesired state or were not going to 'act out' the behaviour. A sub-modality link is created from image (1) to image (2), so that if the mind picks up the trigger in image (1), it automatically takes the client to the second image/state (2); thus changing the state from an un-resourceful to a resourceful one.

Tom: When I first picked up this session to read the thought went through my head, 'SWISH and MS … This will be interesting!' A simple technique being used with such a horribly debilitating problem. Then I remembered that Mark had wanted help to feel more balanced and think more positively – not to cure his MS. It can be easy to get swept along with the diagnosis and not what the client wants.

The effects of MS are incredibly frightening. I see immense fear in clients who do not know how their lives are going to end up; angry and frustrated that nothing can help; and that their future is out of their hands. It is heartbreaking to hear. This is what took me straight to the problem, initially overlooking what Mark was actually looking for from therapy.

The choice of SWISH is effective for a visual client and fits well with someone who knows what they *don't* want to think and feel and what they *do* want to experience instead. Sometimes a lot of work needs to be done to get us to just this point, but Mark appears open and ready for this change.

The Session

Sandra: How have things been going since we last met?

Mark: Really good actually. I feel much more relaxed generally. Little things don't seem to irritate me so much. It was great to remember how to relax and what that feels like for me. I'm doing it every night before I go to bed.

Sandra: Last time we talked about looking at the 'negative head' that you experience. Does that still seem the most helpful thing to work on?

This was a specific working hypothesis that we had agreed on, but I wanted to check that in the light of his response to the first session this was still what he felt would be most helpful.

> **Tom:** Sandra remains with what Mark was asking for – helping him with his responses to his world. She checks with Mark at the beginning of the session that what they had planned was still important for him. The sessions need to be client led and here we see Sandra modelling the fact that 'nothing is set in stone' and that it is okay to change one's mind; that it is about the 'now' and what is needed.

Mark: Yes that would be good. I can still feel it is there. It's quite a physical experience. It's when I feel really tired and my knees feel heavy, even though it's first thing in the morning. It reminds me that I've got limits and the reality of my situation. I want to walk in the morning but because of how I feel I can't.

Sandra: Are there any other times that this negative head occurs apart from in the morning?

I need to gain more sense of his experience of this negativity and thus I look to obtain further examples.

Mark: When the phone rings at work, it's like I'm expecting the worst, a threat to my livelihood.

Sandra: If you could sum up in one word the experience of this negative state, what would it be?

Mark: Worry … (silence). Worry about whatever I am doing going wrong. I always think of the worst-case scenario when I am in this place. I doubt everything and I get very frustrated.

Mark gives a couple of examples that are work related, describing the worry as expecting a 'spanner in the works'.

Sandra: I've noticed all of these examples are work related.

Mark: Yes, it's mainly at work that I get like this. The stress of being self-employed and building a business. Feeling as tired as I have been means that I only have a certain amount of energy as well.

Sandra: So when you are negative you feel worried, threatened, doubting and frustrated. How do you act when you are in this place?

Mark: I get hassled and feel rushed. I'm constantly having to think ahead to go through the 'what if's'.

Sandra: I'm feeling exhausted just thinking about how this is for you!

Mark: You should try it some time! (He smiles.)

Mark continues in a more descriptive way to explain what this is like for him.

Tom: This intervention seems to touch Mark in a powerful way and he continues to invite Sandra into his world using more richly descriptive language.

Sandra: Can you create an image that represents this state for you?

Mark: That's easy. I am sitting in my car, frowning and feeling very tense, gripping the steering wheel.

Sandra: What particularly do you notice about this image? What tells you that you are really in this negative state?

Here I am now looking for the trigger submodality – something that I can use to connect this negative state to the desired state.

Mark: It's the tension in my face and my clenched jaw.

Sandra: Okay, that's good. How do you know when you are going to go into this state? Teach me how *I* would know when to do this.

> **Tom:** This is always a powerful and potent way of helping a client describe in detail how they get to their place of 'being', in Mark's case, his negative mindset.

Mark: You would do this when you feel tired. You see, it would remind you that you only have limited resources and you have so much to get done. I *have* to go to work and also find time for my family.

We really are gaining a sense of what it is like for Mark. When he feels tired, this triggers the negative state, which is one of worry, doubt and tension. I surmise that feeling tired reminds him of the reality of himself and his situation. This exploration may come later. I also sense (by his use of words) that when he is in a negative state he has gone out of the 'now', no longer in the present, instead jumping between the past and the future (what if's).

In this session, however, we are working on helping him take some control of the states that are unhelpful for him and so I make a mental note of my processing and continue with the technique. The first image is not early enough in the sequence of becoming negative as he is linking this to feeling tired and is thus already in the state. We need to create an image *just before* his negative mindset appears.

Sandra: Okay. Can you give me an image of you 'realising' that you are feeling tired?

Mark describes an image of him becoming aware that his knees are aching and he feels lethargic. There is also awareness that he is feeling unsteady. The trigger modality then is the feeling in his legs.

Sandra: Now can you tell me how you would like to be in this situation instead.

The fact of the matter is that Mark *is* going to feel tired at times and I want to create an image that represents a different 'response' to feeling tired.

Mark: I want to be able to step back and be rational. To relax a little. I would like to be able to think 'whatever will be will be' and be more confident in myself.

Sandra: That's great. Can you create an image that represents this?

Mark: I have two that come to mind: me with my wife and sons, carefree, strolling in the park; and me just sitting and chatting at work. I'm sitting back, natural and relaxed.

Sandra: Tell me more about them. What do you notice that tells you that you are relaxed, rational and immersed into what sounds like, to me, a philosophical place about life and you?

Mark: I'm smiling, relaxed and casual. I look natural and there are no pressures in either picture. No time constraints.

Sandra: It looks like you are right in the 'moment' in these images, enjoying the now with your family.

Mark: Yes that's just it. No time constraints, relaxed, casual and natural.

Sandra: Right … if you would like to close your eyes, you can begin to enjoy some relaxation right now, knowing that no one wants anything, no one needs anything and no one expects anything.

Mark settles down and I take him through a bodily relaxation (focusing in particular on the muscles in his face and jaw). I take him into a further visualisation of a healing garden where he can experience a deep sense of peace, tranquillity and healing.

Sandra: Now what I want you to do is to create the image of the moment when you are recognising that you are feeling tired, and when you have it, just nod your head and let me know … (He nods.) That's good. Now I want you to put that image in a corner of your mind so that we can come back to it in a moment. Now I want you to create another image of you feeling carefree, relaxed and strolling. Where you are smiling and have no pressures, or maybe you would like to create an image of you sitting and chatting … I wonder which one will give you the most relaxed and natural experience that you need here?

Mark: Both of them.

Sandra: That's great. Let's use both of them. Can you hold both of them in an image in front of you?

Mark: Yes … I have a split screen so the images are now side by side.

Sandra: Brilliant. Now I want you to put the images in a different corner of your mind and bring forward the first one and I want you to focus on the feelings in your legs. I wonder if it is an ache or a twinge or maybe something else?

Mark: It's a dull ache.

Sandra: Okay … focus on the dull ache and then in a moment I am going to count to 3 and say the word 'SWISH' and at that moment I want you to change this image to the double image of you relaxing, talking, strolling and enjoying the moment. 1 … 2 … 3 … SWISH … and focus on these images, noticing the smile on your face, the look in your eyes, how comfortable and casual you feel, carefree, just enjoying your family and being at work.

Now bring forward the first 'tired' image, focusing on the feelings in your knees and then when I count to 3, this image will change to the double image … and you may even notice that these pictures are brighter, lighter and more in focus … incredibly colourful and seemingly all around you. (Enhancing the submodalities to give the images more intensity and association.) 1 … 2 … 3 … SWISH … and just notice all the things in these images that show your philosophical thinking, the confidence you have in yourself, and really immerse yourself in both of them.

I take Mark through the same SWISH process five or six more times enhancing the second images and suggesting the decline of the first. He then tells me that he can hardly get hold of the first image now, which tells me that the mental re-programming is well under way.

Sandra: That's brilliant. Well done. Step inside one of the relaxing images now and really feel how it is being you right in the moment, enjoying life, enjoying spending time with your family and enjoying the feeling of being relaxed and natural.

I continue with post-hypnotic suggestions about practising the technique daily and engaging the subconscious mind to notice when he is feeling relaxed and calm more and more, suggesting that his subconscious mind, from now on, will explore other times in his life when he feels naturally carefree, smiling and relaxed, and to be able to use the images whenever he needs them. Then I bring the client back to a full state of awareness.

Mark: Absolutely brilliant. The two images of me relaxing were great. When I tried them on, I really could feel so much slower and more relaxed. That's how I want to be; otherwise I miss out on things. It was so much easier being me in the second image.

Sandra: You worked the technique really well. (It felt right to praise Mark here and encourage him to gain confidence in his ability to use his mind.) I have noticed that pressure and time are words that you have used quite a lot in this session.

Mark: Yes … I do seem to have done. I do think I put myself under a lot of pressure at work. I am such a perfectionist and want the people that contract me to do their work to be really happy with what I have done. I also put myself under some pressure when wanting to spend time with my family.

Sandra: It's like time is both precious and pressured? (Mark smiled.) If you can practise the technique at home and perhaps be curious about when you feel pressured and when you feel relaxed, noticing what the difference is and when they occur, that would be helpful for our next session.

Mark: Thank you very much for this. It was great.

> **Tom:** Sandra's responses, encouragement and praise would (I imagine) have gone a long way to building Mark's confidence, especially as she shared an important observation about time being 'precious and pressured', which appeared to resonate with him.
>
> We also see a perfectionist side of Mark coming through that is quite powerful. This may be helpful to explore and work with at some point in the future via some parts therapy work.

The Processing of the Session

SWISH seemed to work well for Mark as the technique increased his level of awareness. It felt as if we were working at two levels:

one at the state changing level and the other at a much deeper existential phenomenological level, exploring his experience of temporality, choice and responsibility.

Mark was learning and adjusting to something that was most certainly uncertain. To be faced with such a medical condition was, for me, unthinkable and I shared in the fears that were very present in the room, but which he clearly didn't want or need to talk about right now. Why should he? Right now he was learning to be with himself and understand his needs for health and well-being. With me, he wanted to understand a little more about being in the present and being more in control of his feelings. These sessions were not about suppressing his feelings but understanding them and knowing how to nurture himself through them rather than becoming locked in one state. I thought about how unfair life can be sometimes, but also how out of suffering can come an inner strength and the opportunity to really look at life and what you want from it. This seemed to be what Mark was doing.

What Happened Next?

At the next session Mark told me he had started walking again and was beginning to feel better in himself, hardly experiencing any negative times and generally feeling stronger. He was realising, however, that he rushed everywhere and that he needed to re-learn 'slowing down'. This led to the exploration of an inner conflict he held about living in the short term and yet with the long-term future ever present. Short term he desired to live life to the full and long term he wanted to make sure he was investing for his future.

We explored this conflict using psycho-imaginative therapy (PIT). Mark's different parts were represented as animals as a way to focus on how these could work together towards a symbolic agreement creating an inner harmony between these conflicting personality parts. After this process he said he felt much better and more in control of life, and was where he wanted to be. We parted company at the fifth session, the work he needed and wanted to do finished. I have heard from a new referral that six months on Mark is continuing to thrive.

Tom: Sandra stayed with what Mark brought to therapy. He was not asking to go deep into an exploration of his MS, and Sandra, while appreciating the bigger picture, doesn't get sidelined by it.

It sounds as if Mark really benefited from these sessions and it is wonderful to hear some feedback as to how he was six months later, as we don't always bear witness to the outcomes of our work. I have a sense that Sandra gave Mark just what he needed at this time, and that if he wanted to explore further, he would know just who to ask.

Chapter 3

Working Creatively with Imagery

Dream Work (Sandra)

> *You see things; and you say, 'Why?' But I dream things that never were; and I say, 'Why not?'*
> George Bernard Shaw

Dreams often leave us, in the moments when we are waking, with fragments that bemuse us as to their origin, or they leave us with stories that question why our inner mind has taken part in such an intricate and complicated narrative when our waking day life is kept so organised and planned.

Sigmund Freud (1856–1939) suggested that this was *exactly* the reason we dream: to allow our mind to shut out the realities of life and reach the unconscious mind's forbidden thoughts and unfulfilled desires. In Freud's (1900) view, dreams hold two elements: the *manifest content*, the story we are able to recall and describe to another; and the *latent content*, the meaning behind the story, our unconscious thoughts and desires undistinguishable in the detail – and which leave us wanting when we try to work out what our dream is really about.

In Freudian psychoanalysis the aim is to work with clients' dreams by interpreting them, transforming the manifest content into the latent content and attempting to find meaning in the symbolic images presented to us. In this way Freud believed we can find answers to the unconscious messages held within the dream and resolve the unconscious conflicts originating in early childhood.

> *Dreams say what they mean, but they*
> *don't say it in daytime language.*
> Gail Godwin

However, this is not the only approach to understanding dreams. Carl Jung (1875–1961) saw dreams as a 'window' into the unconscious, offering solutions to everyday living through understanding them and reflecting our inner drive towards health and maturity, which he termed as 'individuation'.

He identified different types of dreams: those that simply process our 'everydayness' and are fluctuations of the psychic balance, and others that are connected to 'universal' (or common) themes and symbolic experiences spanning all cultures. Jung described these themes as 'archetypes', deriving from the 'collective unconscious' and tending to occur at critical phases in our life. The archetypes appear in dreams as symbolic images – ideas and beliefs passed down through generations – which guide us through our personal experiences of life.

For example, we may find ourselves experiencing the persona, the public mask we put on in life; the shadow, the 'hidden' side of us that rears its unappealing head on occasions when we least expect it and when we hear ourselves saying 'I don't know what came over me' or 'I just wasn't myself'; or the anima/animus, the female/male aspects of us that we resonate with in relation to the opposite sex.

In his approach to dream work we are able to explore the symbolic archetypal images we encounter, and attempt to resolve and integrate them in relation to ourselves and our life circumstances.

> *Dreams are illustrations … from the book*
> *your soul is writing about you.*
> Marsha Norman

Yet another approach to dreams is through the work of Fritz Perls (1893–1970) and Laura Perls (1905–1990) who, in their theoretical and practical development of Gestalt psychotherapy, explored how they could work with dreams on an *intrapersonal* level. In

Gestalt dream work we can discover aspects of us that we have 'rejected' or 'disowned', as this approach believes that every object and every character within the dream represents a part of the self.

In this way we can uncover the meaning of the parts and connect with our deeper feelings and energies that we have rejected, and thus discover and integrate more of who and what we are at a deeper and more intrinsic level.

> *Dreams are today's answers to tomorrow's questions.*
> Edgar Cayce

While the theories of Freud, Jung and many others have contributed to our understanding of dreams, the Gestalt approach fits perfectly with hypnotic trance work, as aspects of the dream (aspects of ourselves) can be set free. In hypnosis the client explores the dream from different positions or frames of reference, allowing the disowned aspects to be revealed, experienced, expressed and integrated in a symbolic way, thus creating a more fully functioning person.

Let's get a sense of how it works.

Looking for Something More in Life

The Client's Presenting Problem

Alex had been taking stock, looking back at her life and wanting to make changes for a better future; her past, present and future all vying for attention and striving for some semblance of order. Alex told me she had dreamt a strange and powerful dream over the last few months which had remained with her, and she was wondering what the dream meant; it seemed such a 'nice' dream, even more pertinent considering aspects of her life were currently quite challenging.

When someone enters therapy, and in particular hypnotherapy, they come face to face with their inner world, re-visiting, re-assessing and re-processing vast amounts of material. It is not surprising for a client to dream vividly, often becoming excited and anxious to tell us what happened in their dream and hoping we can make some sense of it for them.

The Session

Alex: I've been reflecting quite a lot about my life and have been feeling quite sad. I want to make some changes and I feel ready for that, but I'm not yet sure what direction I want to go in. I don't feel I have come to terms with some of my past and I want to find some peace with things that have happened. I had this dream a couple of weeks ago that was extremely vivid, which showed a beautiful garden in which I felt so peaceful and where I felt loved; it was just wonderful. That's how I want to feel. It was such a nice dream.

Sandra: When you described the dream your face just relaxed and you seemed like you were re-experiencing something quite profound.

Bringing in 'how' Alex is presenting the material as this usually leads to the 'now'.

Alex: The garden was so lovely that I feel really peaceful when I think about it. I don't ever feel that peaceful in my life at the moment. Everything's just worry and upset, and more worry.

At this point I was tempted to explore what worry and upset was like for my client, but I would have then been entangled in the content. It may have been helpful for Alex to off-load her week, but this could have steered us away from the opportunity to explore her deeper sense of self.

Sandra: Can you take me through the dream and describe it to me?

It is important to explore the dream 'pre' hypnosis as it allows the client to verbalise the material and to begin revealing the deeper meanings within it. It also gives us a chance to 'feel' the dream and to be aware of the work that we may be approaching once in hypnosis, thus offering a sense of safety.

Alex: The dream starts in a building that I work in. Everyone is getting on with things and I am talking to a couple of people making arrangements for lunch. Lunchtime comes and we all make our way down the stairs and out of the building. All of a sudden everyone goes off in another direction and I am left on my own. I decide to go towards a park and find myself in a beautiful garden with many historical statues. I spend time looking at the statues, feeling peaceful and I then notice a fountain in the distance, so I walk towards it. The water is lovely and clear and I scoop some up with my hands to drink it, but as I put it to my mouth, it turns to rubber. I try to bite into it, but I can't. Then the dream ends.

I let the client tell the dream from start to finish uninterrupted. I want to hear it as a complete experience and allow myself to 'feel' the dream and let my thoughts wander and wonder through the description.

I wondered about Alex being left by her friends, the meaning of the historical figures and the water that turned to rubber when she tried to drink it. I was aware of feeling sad as she told me the dream and also surprised at how the fountain was not what it first seemed. I held these thoughts and feelings and remembered that at the start of the session she said this was a nice dream! It all sounded so picturesque and beautiful at one level and yet I was experiencing deeper feelings of sadness and aloneness at another. Having acknowledged my thoughts and feelings, there was then a need to explore how Alex felt.

Tom: As I began to read this session I was curious to read that Alex's dream was both 'nice' and yet strange, so I began initially to expect a horror story, which shows my own personal experiences of strange dreams!

I am often asked to give my interpretation of a dream by someone who is wondering about its meaning: 'You're a therapist, so what does my dream mean?' In reality my interpretation of someone else's dream is of little use. I am often tempted, however, because interpreting a dream can be a fascinating process.

As I read this session I began to notice the vast number of questions coming into my mind, which made me think about how often I hear therapists sharing with each other that they have so many questions about a client, and assume this is hindering the therapy process. It is important to remember that without questions you are unlikely to find answers.

Sandra: What emotions do you experience in the dream, Alex?

Alex: I feel upset when I find that my friends have gone off and left me, then peaceful in the park but a bit in awe of the beauty of it. I then feel frustrated that I can't drink the water and neither can I bite the rubber.

In my mind I began to engage in making sense of the story, wondering whether there was something that she wasn't able to swallow or get her teeth into, or that maybe nothing was ever what it seemed to her.

Sandra: So you moved through being upset, peaceful and frustrated.

Alex: Well, when I say frustrated, it is more like surprised that it is rubber and not water. I keep trying to bite it, but I can't. I'm confused as I don't know how it has solidified and I don't like it much.

Sandra: What are you thinking as you try to drink it and realise it has solidified?

The client has focused on the end of the dream as we explored the emotional content, so I stayed with what seemed important to her.

Alex: I am thinking, 'What has happened? Why can't I bite it? What am I going to do now?'

Sandra: So it brings up questions for you?

Alex: Oh yes.

Sandra: Are these questions that you are asking yourself in your life at the moment?

Alex: Goodness, yes. A lot of 'why' questions actually.

Sandra: So what did the dream ask of you?

Alex: That's a good question. I don't really know. I suppose it's asking me to make time for myself and to find some peace within. I didn't realise that there was so much to this dream.

Sandra: Goodness, I feel *I* am asking a lot of questions! But can I ask one more question and then if you like we can explore the dream in hypnosis. What title would you give the dream?

This helps place the dream in the context of the inner world of the client.

Alex: The Journey.

> **Tom:** I hear myself saying, 'Do you need to bite it?', as Alex says she can't bite the rubber. Sandra, though, stays with reflecting the story, to remain open and offering Alex the opportunity to seek answers to her questions. She acknowledges at this point the number of questions flying around the room as she then asks just one more! I may have stayed with this for a while longer. I begin to wonder just how 'heady' the room felt at this stage and how acknowledging this in the session would have impacted upon it.

Alex was then guided into hypnosis. I ask Alex to dream 'The Journey' and to nod her head when she has finished. Alex nods.

Sandra: Now I want you to describe the dream again as if it is happening now.

Here is where I can begin to encourage the client to describe her thoughts and feelings at a deeper level.

Alex: I am in the office and we are planning what we are going to do at lunchtime.

Sandra: How are you feeling?

Alex: Good. I like these people, they are my friends and we are going for lunch together.

Sandra: What's happening there now?

Keeping the client in the 'now' of the dream by using language that suggests this is the case.

Alex: We are going down the stairs and out of the building and then all of a sudden everyone walks in the opposite direction and I am left alone.

Sandra: What's that like?

It is important to keep interventions short and simple, so that the focus is on the client's experience.

Alex: I feel alone … I don't understand why they have left me … I'm upset … But then I see there is a park and I'm walking off towards it … It is beautiful, full of historical statues.

Sandra: Just describe some of the statues.

Alex: Well they are all in pairs, like couples, from different eras. There is one that looks like Henry VIII with one of his wives.

> **Tom:** As I follow the hypnotic session I am reminded just how much our own curiosity creeps into sessions. As I drift off … and start to wonder if the statue of Henry VIII's wife has a head or not? A good example of the need for rapid 'bracketing' at times!

Sandra: What are you thinking as you look at the statues?

Alex: How lovely and happy they all look together. They are couples. This is a beautiful garden, I like it in here. I'm wandering around and looking at all the statues. Then I notice a fountain which looks lovely as it glistens in the sunshine. I'm walking towards it and see the water around the bottom … I cup my hands and scoop up the water. I try to drink it but it has turned hard. I try to bite it but I can't.

Sandra: Can you describe what the water has become in your hands?

Alex: It's like a rubbery substance.

Sandra: How are you feeling as you hold the substance?

Alex: Confused, I don't understand, but I keep trying to bite it.

Sandra: What makes you keep biting it even though it seems that you can't?

Alex: I don't know. It's like I feel I must keep trying. I'm determined.

I now have heard the dream in hypnosis and she has been able to verbalise the finer details of it with her thoughts and feelings being described alongside. As this part of the session happens, I imagine *myself* in the dream, noticing how I feel and where my thoughts take me. Clearly the fountain is significant and I know that I will need to explore this further but I am also drawn to the garden of historical statues.

Sandra: Okay. I would like you to start the dream again and tell me what is happening.

She again describes the start as she comes out of the building, with the crowd about to go off in the other direction.

Sandra: On the count of 3, I want you to become the crowd of people … 1, 2, 3 … and, as the crowd, you look at Alex and tell me what happens now in the dream.

Alex: Well, we start to go off in the other direction and leave her there.

Sandra: Why do you leave her there?

Alex: I don't know, we just do.

Sandra: Do you know her?

Alex: No, not really.

Sandra: Okay, on the count of 3, I want you to become Alex again, watching the group leave … 1, 2, 3.

I don't feel there is any more that can be gained from exploring this part of the dream from the other perspective. It feels more helpful to focus back on the client.

Sandra: As you watch them go. How does it feel for you?

Alex: I'm upset. I'm on my own ... (silence). I feel like I have been rejected. (Alex begins to cry. Silence.) I don't understand. I am on my own again.

Further silence. At this moment 'on my own again' feels very painful.

Sandra: Now what's happening?

Alex: I see there is a park and I make my way over there. It's beautiful.

She describes the park with the statues in it.

Sandra: As you stand there, you will be drawn to one particular pair of statues. Make your way over there now.

Alex: I'm going over to a couple that don't look particularly rich but look very much in love.

Sandra: On the count of 3 I would like you to become one of the statues ... 1, 2, 3 ... and now continue the dream.

Alex: I see a very sad lady looking at me.

Sandra: What would you like to say to her?

Alex: Don't be sad. We are with you. You have us. (Alex cries.)

Sandra: On the count of 3 you will change back into Alex looking at the statue ... 1, 2, 3. What's happening for you?

This felt a very poignant moment for my client and it needed to be acknowledged and verbalised.

Alex: I feel so alone, although it's lovely to feel that I have people with me that love me. It's quite overwhelming. I *do* have people who love and care for me.

Sandra: Is there anything you would like to say back to the statue?

Alex: Thank you.

Sandra: I want you to just spend a few moments surrounded by people who love and care for you. Just allow yourself to feel how it feels surrounded by love and care.

I cannot say why I felt this was important at the time, apart from it felt a moment was needed to be in the 'love and care' of the statues and of the people in her life who love her.

Sandra: Tell me what's happening now.

Alex: I see the fountain and begin to walk towards it.

Sandra: Okay. On the count of 3 I would like you to become the fountain … 1, 2, 3. Now tell me what's happening in the dream.

Alex: I see a woman walking towards me. She stands and looks at my water.

Sandra: Are you all water?

Alex: No, at the bottom there are hard bits, but she doesn't know that. She puts her hands in the water and scoops up from the bottom.

Sandra: And on the count of 3, I would like you to become the hard bits that have just been scooped up … 1, 2, 3.

Alex: I'm being picked up and … she is trying to eat me! (Alex sounds bemused.)

Sandra: What's that like?

Alex: I don't want her to. What is she doing that for? (She looks angry now.)

Sandra: You sound angry.

Alex: Well I am. I don't want to be eaten.

Sandra: Can you describe yourself to me?

Alex: I am kind of like rubber. I am clear but solid. I am indestructible.

Sandra: On the count of 3 I want you to become Alex … 1, 2, 3. I want you to look at the rubber you are holding and tell me what it looks like, along with any other thoughts that come to mind as you hold it.

Alex: It's like a teardrop … it's quite beautiful really. I hadn't realised. I'm thinking I don't want to eat it now.

Sandra: So what would you like to do now?

Alex: I would like to take it home with me and show it to people and keep it on my mantelpiece. It is like a beautiful crystal.

Sandra: On the count of 3 I would like you to become the rubber teardrop …1, 2, 3. Alex wants to keep you and take you home to share with people. Is there anything you would like to say to her?

Alex: She needs to remember me and she needs not to swallow me. I have energy and I can bounce high in the sky. I'm her friend.

Sandra: On the count of 3 I would like you to become Alex …1, 2, 3. How would you like to respond?

Alex: I am going to bounce it on the ground. Goodness, it has gone *really* high … I'll chase after it and then I am going home. (She is smiling.)

Sandra: Okay, as you make your way home, I would like you to go back through the beautiful garden and share your beautiful object with the statues.

I remind her again of all the people who love her and how the rubber crystal is beautiful and that she may like to keep it close to her from now on, and I then bring her out of hypnosis.

The Processing of the Session

Upon opening her eyes, Alex said 'Wow!' She had been unaware of the emotional depth held within the dream and the sadness about feeling alone and also how unloved she felt as a child and the anger this brought up towards her mother. Consequently she always found it difficult to allow people into her life.

Alex realised that she had learnt as a child not to be emotional and that she should 'swallow' her emotions. 'It's alright to cry. That's amazing,' she said as she both smiled and began to cry. I asked Alex about the beautiful garden and the statues whereupon she commented on how powerful those images were, reminding her of how so many people loved her. I commented on the rubber ball, wondering what 'part' of her this was. She felt it was all about the tears that she had not shared, even with herself. She was glad she now had this part on her mantelpiece as it was quite beautiful, like a crystal. She smiled as she said she wanted to show this crystal to her friends.

We closed the session by exploring what she would take away from our meeting. She said, being able to cry and feel emotional, sharing her tears as she had already experienced with me. 'It's okay to cry,' she finished, smiling.

> **Tom:** Sandra describes how she imagines herself 'within' the dream which is a really helpful process as it reaches out towards a sense of the client's inner world. The way she gives Alex time to experience the love and care feels so necessary and the description of the processing of the session shows me how this approach achieves such depth and a level of realisation and insight all in just one session. 'It's okay to cry,' Alex says and I tingle when I read this, sensing the innocence of her words.

This was one of those sessions where I had tears in my eyes, needing to hold them within (only just), connecting with my own emotions while allowing space for Alex. I felt so sad and at a loss for words at times with her longing to be in such a relationship, perhaps showing how deeply felt this was for *her*. There was a richness in her dream that caught me by surprise, allowing a feeling of connectedness with her during the dream work. However, upon opening her eyes, I became aware of how I began to feel disconnected, as if we had moved to a different level of un-relating. I felt a little awkward during the processing; wanting to allow Alex to share her tears but unsure as to what she needed. I kept in mind however that she was only just learning to be emotional with another person and wondered how awkward that was for her too and if she knew what she needed. This would be something important to explore in future sessions.

After a session like this there was a need to spend time at our next meeting exploring how the experience had been absorbed, as well as how she had been feeling during the week, and this we did. What was important for this client was to focus on exploring how emotions are experienced and being able to be at one with them. Alex mentioned she needed to find peace within her story; and here lay the main bulk of our future work, as she began narrating her story and exploring how this defined her way of being in the world, and thus finding a more authentic self along the way.

Tom: What Sandra writes about at the end of the session shows just how valuable an awareness of oneself is in the constant and ever present client–therapist relationship. As she explores the hypnotic session she becomes aware of feeling disconnected, which can tell us much about the client's level of engagement with others, as the real experiencing of being with Alex comes to the fore.

This session feels so full of content and, at the same time, deep with emotional connections which Sandra guides Alex through. Working with dreams here was ideal for Alex in her search for deeper meaning in her experiencing of life.

Guided Affective Imagery (Sandra)

> *Imagination is more important than knowledge.*
> *For knowledge is limited to all we now*
> *know and understand, while imagination*
> *embraces the entire world, and all there*
> *ever will be to know and understand.*
> Albert Einstein

For over a century now, imagery in psychotherapy has been used as a symbolic way to make sense of unconscious material; imagery being a range of techniques from simple visualisations and direct imagery-based suggestion through to metaphor and story telling. From imagining you are on a beach watching a beautiful sunset and feeling at peace, or imaging how you feel as an 'animal', or entering a cave and meeting your very own inner advisor ready to tell you something that you need to hear, through to the famous ugly duckling story where one becomes a beautiful swan, imagery can effectively help clients to connect with their inner self.

Freud and Breuer's famously documented case of 'Anna O' in *Studies on Hysteria* (1895) offers us the first glimpse into the power of the imagination. Freud theorised that when the mind is fearful and overly emotional (i.e. hysterical), a person might 'imagine' experiencing disease symptoms.

For many years research has been exploring the effectiveness of guided imagery in the therapeutic setting, most concluding that it enhances learning, healing and performing. In fact, as Utay and Miller (2006) write: 'It has earned the right to be considered a research-based approach to helping.'

However, it is important to note that this method of exploration was not created purely within the psychological field; it has deeper roots in Native American, Hindu, Judeo-Christian and other religious traditions, as well as in traditional Chinese medicine, to name but a few. For us, this signifies the universal depth of imagery.

The use of imagery became more specifically therapeutic in the work of Kretschmer (1922), who began adapting the use of daydreams in therapy, referring to these inner visions as thinking in the form of a 'movie'.

Then Jacob Moreno's (1889–1974) development of psychodrama in the 1940s shone a light upon our understanding of how 'guiding' the externalisation of the client's internal process through imagery offers insights and resolutions, with participants re-enacting the imagination of the client's problem on the setting of a stage.

Hanscarl Leuner (1954) further developed psychodrama into what he called guided affective imagery (GAI). This helps the client to symbolically connect with their internal cognitive, affective and somatic resources. The aim is not to provide images for the client to judge or eradicate, but simply to explore and use them, as they represent the 'inner world' that language may not be able to capture. In guiding the client to work with imagery and discover its meaning, there is a potential for deepening self-awareness. Once we *really* 'know' something, then choices become available to us.

Guided imagery can prove a particularly effective method when we feel that greater insights are needed into the presenting problem as it can help to creatively describe it and position it in the client's world as a whole.

The method can be useful when we find ourselves 'stuck' with the progress of therapy and are seeking to find out what is happening for the client on a deeper level, out of their conscious awareness. Often these impasses occur when we are ourselves trying to work out where we need to be heading in therapy from an overly conscious and logical level.

Guided imagery can be essential in helping clients who lack connection with their creativity and imagination to open up to more than a logical and cognitive experience, where they can creatively find their own solutions.

> *Logic will get you from A to B. Imagination*
> *will take you everywhere.*
> Albert Einstein

The meaning derived from the images our clients explore in imagery work is designed to help them acknowledge subconscious motivations, to become aware of the significance of the symbols they uncover and shed light on possible areas of resistance they are holding within.

In GAI there are ten standard imaginary situations, ranging from basic structured images such as the meadow, onto which just about any problem the client has can be projected, through to more highly structured images which are designed to explore specific areas such as sexuality or anger. Some of the more structured imagery scenarios are designed solely to elicit deeply repressed material, as in a 'figure' rising out of the murky waters of a swamp.

As well as the meadow scenario, other basic imagery methods include climbing a mountain, which is used to elicit the client's feelings about their mastery of life, or following a brook to its source, to get a sense of the flow of the client's psychic energy. More structured scenarios are made up of variations of exploring a house, coming across a close relative, a long walk in the countryside on a lonely road, a lion in a cage or a forest, the client's ego ideal (who/how they want to be) or the client looking into a dark forest or the opening of a cave. Each one has its own symbolic meaning and can help us to uncover unconscious material that ordinarily we wouldn't elicit through conventional counselling or psychotherapy.

> *Some people say they haven't yet found*
> *themselves. But the self is not something*
> *one finds; it is something one creates.*
> Thomas Szasz

Along with further methods of guiding and managing the client's symbolic material, GAI offers us a rich insight into our clients' internal processes, uncovering unconscious feelings, wishes and desires, the content of which often surprises even them. This powerful uncovering of their 'inner world' leads to deeper insight into their 'self' and along with that, the possibility of change.

We can see this process in action in the GAI session (the mountain) below.

Eating Problems: Bulimia

The Client's Presenting Problem

Anna (23) contacted me via email asking if I had experience of working with bulimia, which I had, and so after a couple of emails she booked her first session. I wondered about her use of emails, as they said very little and felt rather detached. I was mindful that she had chosen to keep her distance as we were just 'text' on a screen so far. This was to prove important later on, as I found she continually avoided being in a relationship with me and was ultimately able to detach and leave therapy abruptly, angrily and without any apparent difficulty.

The first session revealed Anna had been bulimic since she was 12 years old and that she was not really sure why or how this started. This raised doubts in me initially, as in my previous experience of clients' descriptions of bulimia they could easily recall when the behaviour first began. However, this was the first time Anna had told her story to anybody so I needed to just sit back and listen.

Anna shared that at the time the behaviour started she was being bullied at school and was experiencing difficulties in her relationship with her mother. She also mentioned her present-day situation: having achieved a first-class business degree she was now working twelve-hour days in a job where performance and pay were target related, bringing a level of stress to her life. She lived in a flat with her sister and had never been in a close relationship.

Anna talked about her regular bingeing and vomiting cycle at work and at home, especially when bored or if she had eaten too much. I asked her how this helped and she told me that it was a way of gaining comfort and of avoiding her feelings of insecurity and worry. She also admitted that it was easier to keep on doing it rather than change the behaviour. She *wanted* to stop being bulimic, although the thought of actually achieving this was terrifying for her. However, she felt she had reached a time where this behaviour was holding her back and she now wanted to do more with her life.

I asked her what she felt would help, to which she responded that she needed to let go of perfectionism and paranoia, to take life less seriously and to be more confident in being herself. Forty minutes into this first session, and beginning to focus on what Anna wanted and what she felt would make a difference, I was struggling. I was running out of questions and could not seem to find the words that would encourage her to talk openly about herself and her difficulties. She seemed happy to answer any direct questions put forward but appeared to find it hard to say more than a few words in reply.

I wrote in my notes at the end of this initial session: 'I am left not knowing much at all about Anna. I feel shocked, shattered and sick. I am upset at how bad the session has been and how useless I feel I have come across. I am sure that she won't want to see me again!' I met Tom not long after this session and his first words were, 'My goodness, what has happened to you? You look traumatised!'

Not many clients leave me feeling like Anna did. In the session I had found it hard to connect with her, although there was no obvious reason for this. The harder I tried to shake the feelings off, the worse they became. There was a mild anxiousness at the start of the session as she answered my questions, which gradually increased in intensity as the session unfolded; and as I couldn't identify anything specific that could leave me feeling so unsure, I became even more anxious.

In my experience of working with eating disorders, I have found that clients often carry intense inner world experiences. Anna had a profound effect on me and, after this wore off a little, I wanted to reflect on what had happened, needing to make sense of it all. However, this was only our first meeting and I was aware that if I made any unfounded assumptions about her in my search for clarity, I would be closing myself off rather than opening myself up to her. Therefore I had to be content with not knowing and feeling instead some of what perhaps led her to vomiting (I certainly felt very sick). One question I asked myself was whether Anna was finding it hard to be in therapy; another was whether it was me that was finding it difficult to be with Anna and, if so, why.

Tom: When I started to read this session I quickly became involved in Anna's story and was reminded that in my own work with clients I encounter much passion, along with equal amounts of angst. The initial session touched many of the profound experiences I myself have had with those suffering with bulimia, anorexia and other forms of eating disorder, with these clients very often remaining in my mind long after therapy has ended.

Sandra described how she struggled in the beginning to be herself and to find words, indicating the impact that Anna had on her, which at first was quite unnerving. Eating disorders show the complexity of the mind well, and I often find a number of common factors are playing themselves out, such as insecurity, fear, anger and distrust.

From Anna's perspective, her bulimia started at school and in her relationship with her mother, and then she described the pressure she felt in her job and her lack of close relationships, showing possibly that her present-day life echoed in some way her earlier experiences.

There is a lot of research about treating patients with bulimia and other eating disorders, with different theories and therapies describing a variety of reasons, motivations, procedures and treatments. Clients presenting with bulimia tend to be very angry (passively or overtly) and will usually, although not knowingly, look to metaphorically 'vomit' over their therapist. Here, Anna failed to turn up to sessions without telling me, would contact me to say she would be late or would tell me she had forgotten her payment right at the end of the session. Other clients have told me, from time to time, that they do not think that I am helping them, even after sharing how much they feel they are progressing, or that therapy (often described as 'it') isn't working and fighting vehemently against all that I say or do. However, in my experience, these are often very passionate people and the depth of their questioning of themselves and their aspirations in life are second to none. If we can keep a client who uses a bulimic way of being in a relationship with us, we are often more than half way there.

Tom: The notes that Sandra writes at the end of her first session show how overwhelming her experience of Anna was, offering us an insight into Anna's sense of fragility in holding more in her life than she was already coping with.

She showed that in the first session her focus was on Anna and not just her bulimia, an important point to remember as it can be so easy to get sucked into focusing entirely on food, eating patterns, weight and everything the client's life entails in relation to bulimia, and in this, the 'person' can easily get lost.

Choosing the Technique

In the second and third sessions we had been working on specific bulimic behaviours as this was the behavioural change that Anna had sought therapy for. We revisited the different trigger situations in order to use hypnotic suggestion work to help begin to change the specific cycle of thoughts and feelings that led to the bulimic responses.

In the fourth session I used the SWISH technique. It was at this point that issues seemed to be surfacing from a deeper place than in previous meetings, revealing, as Anna described it, a 'big dark green blob' that drew and sucked her in, tempting her with peacefulness, pretending that everything was going to be alright, but when she got there, presenting her with nothingness.

In this session, I was looking to use imagery as she had naturally used imagery the session before. I chose GAI and, in particular, the scenario of the mountain, which traditionally looks to explore someone's aspirations in life: the goals they set, how they are reached, what it is like when they get there and what happens next. I felt this might help us to understand the previous session where she had talked about something drawing her into 'everything's going to be alright, but when she gets there, she is presented with nothingness'.

The Session

At the start of this session Anna said that she had been worrying more than normal. She was fed up of being single, worried about her long working day and about a bullying colleague with whom she worked closely. I could not yet imagine her *in* her life and I didn't yet experience her presence in the room. She was surprised that she wasn't in a relationship, but it was no surprise to me, if how I had found her was similar to how others did – initially awkward to be with.

We focused on how Anna had experienced worry that week, which was about her rather than just her bulimic behaviour. This broadened the spotlight on our work revealing that every aspect of her life was causing anxiety and concern, which was painful for her to bear. After explaining to Anna what I felt would help her in gaining greater enlightenment, and how imagery could assist in creatively finding solutions, we continued.

I took Anna through a short hypnotic induction. I then asked her to imagine a meadow, noticing how beautiful, peaceful and relaxing it was. I led her to a path going off into the distance which I asked her to follow, suggesting she was relaxing further as she strode out with the ground beneath her feet.

Sandra: And in the distance you notice a mountain. Describe it to me.

Anna: It's far away, green and very high. It's like a rolling hill with different levels. It looks very steep.

Sandra: And as you look at this far away green mountain, what are you thinking?

Anna: I am thinking of Greece on holiday when I was 17. I had finished my exams and school, and there was university ahead. I felt carefree, relaxed and so very happy. It was a hopeful time. The people were really nice and friendly and I had no worries. It was so beautiful.

Sandra: That's good, and as you continue your journey, remembering that time in Greece, make your way to the mountain now. When you get to the bottom just let me know … (She nods.) That's good. Now tell me what you notice about the mountain now you are there.

Anna: It looks steep and difficult to climb as it's dangerous and slippery. It's very deep and green. (I note that the words 'deep' and 'green' were also used in the image during our last SWISH session.) The top is very high, overlooking a beautiful kingdom that is bathed in sunlight.

I wonder if that is how life feels for her, that she is always looking at a beautiful life, but not one she is able to experience?

Sandra: Would you like to climb it?

Anna: Yes, I want to get to the top.

Sandra: I want you to begin climbing the mountain and begin to notice what happens.

Anna: I'm following a winding path. It's steep but I am using the rocks to help me. There are little animals. It feels like it is a challenge but I am eager to get up there quickly.

There seems real determination as she uses resources to help her climb. I note that all she is focused on is getting to the top – the journey being irrelevant. I think about how hard it seems for her to be in the present, as she constantly projects herself into the future.

Sandra: Is there anything you need or want?

Here I am looking to draw her back into the now, her journey, encouraging her to get in touch with her wants and needs as she climbs.

Anna: No. I just want to get to the top.

But it is the end that she is interested in and she sounds frustrated with me that it is not quick enough.

Sandra: When you get to the top, tell me what you have.

Anna: I can see the sun. I am very high, almost within the clouds. Below there are smaller mountains. I can see far into the distance, the colours are beautiful. It is clear on one side but there are darker clouds on the other, like rain clouds, they seem to be moving around. It's all very beautiful.

I sense the dynamic nature of being at the top and how she is focused on the clear visual scene before her. I want to know the internal experience of being there and also I am curious about the darker clouds moving around.

Sandra: What are you experiencing as you explore the top of the mountain, Anna?

Anna: I'm satisfied that I have reached the top and I can see now that if I go down the mountain that it will be fine. I wish I could erase everything bad in life … like … get rid of my bulimia. I can see and think of all my dreams up here.

Sandra: What are the dark clouds?

I want to check out the black clouds as this is not something she has mentioned yet.

Anna: This is my bulimia … (Silence.)

I wait for her to say more, leaving a long pause, but she doesn't elaborate.

Sandra: How do you feel?

Anna: I feel hopeful; I feel that it will be okay without the bulimia. I can go down the mountain and it will be fine.

This is the second time she has mentioned going down the mountain. Going back down is okay? It made me think about how Anna had experienced extreme highs and lows in her moods. Is she saying to herself that it is alright to come down in mood? Is being down being without bulimia? Is she saying that it is okay to come back down to life and living? So many thoughts were coming into my mind and I recognised tears rising from within me. I mentally log what has just happened.

Sandra: What do you need to do?

Anna: I need to start acting as if I don't have bulimia. I have to work hard and accept I don't need the eating problem.

I move quickly from feeling tearful to disappointment upon hearing, 'I need to start acting'. Is forcing herself to do something and to work hard at it feasible? Is this just the felt realisation she needed? Is this her taking responsibility for herself?

Tom: There is curiosity about the dark clouds, which did not lead anywhere but to silence from Anna, but we can see from this perhaps how powerful her bulimic experience is, and in this Anna may well have gained some insight, just in this voicing of the bulimia's 'intentions'. This really helped me to get a sense of the forces inside her that she was grappling and battling with. It was certainly something that would need following up in future sessions.

When Anna described how she needed to start acting as if she did not have bulimia and, further, that she did not *need* the eating problem, I too found myself getting stuck, resonating with Sandra's experience. I may at this stage have wanted to explore this further as it seemed rather a simplistic view.

Sandra's exploration of the content of the visualisation feels powerful. 'What are you thinking? Tell me what you notice? Is there anything you need or want? Tell me what you have? What would you like to do now?' all draw out Anna's thoughts and feelings in a solid and direct way, helping her to make the connections she needs and enabling her to express herself.

Sandra: What would you like to do now?

Encouraging the client to choose what is important for her.

Anna: I want to fly and land somewhere where there are smiling faces and warmth.

Sandra: That's good … and so … I don't know if you will gain some wings … or if you will simply allow yourself to lift up into the air like Wonder Woman, but just allow yourself to rise up into the air and now begin to experience the freedom of flight. Feel yourself in control of the speed you are moving at, feel yourself guiding the direction you want to go in. Become aware of the air current as it flows around you. Feel the freedom of going where you want to go and become aware of the scenery below you, in front of you and around you. When you have found the right place to land, then make your way downwards, carefully steering yourself to the ground. When you are there just let me know. (Anna nods.)

Sandra: So Anna … what's it like?

Anna: It's lovely. There are a lot of smiling faces. I know them and yet I don't. They seem familiar in some way. This feels relaxing and I'm happy to be here and they are happy to have me here.

Sandra: Is there anything you would like to do, now that you have landed? It is soon time to return to the meadow.

I was aware that we had fifteen minutes left of the session and that we needed time to process what she had experienced in the hypnotic intervention.

Anna: No … That's it.

Sandra: Then what I would like you to do is to begin to walk onwards, striding out until you find your way back to the meadow. And as you do so, I want you to reflect on this experience and all that you have learnt, because it is useful to utilise the opportunity now to think about what you have experienced – the thoughts, the images, the understandings and the memories – and how you might use all of these things later on from day to day. Because your subconscious mind and your conscious mind can learn from today and I don't know if it will be today, tomorrow or some other time that you will find small things occurring to you from this experience today.

And I don't know just how things are going to change, maybe suddenly over night, or maybe slowly and gradually, but I do know you will be curious to note just what is changing and how you are changing, and so now when you're ready, and not before, in your own time you can gently drift back to the room and open your eyes.

Anna opened her eyes and smiled at me … Silence.

Anna: The climb was very hard, but it was okay as the top was worth it. It's like it gives meaning to what I am doing.

I could have pursued this further and asked her what she meant. In hindsight I should have done but I had my own agenda here, namely those black clouds.

Sandra: The black clouds. I was curious about that.

Anna: It's the bad bits of me, they were moving because they can still take over me and catch me up if they want … The top was so worth it and I'd forgotten the holiday in Greece. I think that was the most free I have ever been. I was happy and content. I do feel different, kind of lighter and stronger. I do feel different.

The client quickly guides me back to where she needs to be as she briefly explains what the black clouds mean and then goes back to talking about being at the top of the mountain. It may mean that today she is avoiding what needed to be explored, or that she simply didn't feel that the clouds were the important part of the experience. I felt it was important to stay with the client and I am pleased that I did.

Sandra: When you were in Greece, how did you find the bulimic behaviour?

Anna: I didn't do it at all out there, it was great. I was happy and had some great friends around me.

Very interesting to note and revisit at a later date. There was a genuineness in her words and her voice during her processing; she was sharing readily and I felt connected with her in these moments as she considered that bulimia did not have to be a part of her life. We drew the session to an end acknowledging how different this session felt for both of us and how it seemed easier for her to share herself. I also asked her to keep revisiting the details of this holiday as it sounded quite amazing. As she was going away on holiday after our session, I hoped this would also be of benefit.

The Processing of the Session

During the hypnotic intervention there were many questions going on in my mind and I noted that I was feeling free to let things unfold in myself and in the session, and to let Anna guide the imagery. I felt moved to tears by the fact that she seemed to realise that bulimia did not have to be part of her life – suggesting this was a very possible reality for her.

Although there was a great deal of material that could have been explored further, I needed to respect her wish to focus on the memories of Mexico and enjoy our new connection together (after all, in Mexico her bulimic behaviour was not present). In talking about this we were anchoring feelings that she had not experienced for a while – freedom and peace. I felt I had connected with Anna and that we now had a closer relationship, but one that would likely be both challenging and overwhelming for her.

What Happened Next?

Sadly, there was only one more session after this. Anna came back from her holiday saying she had enjoyed it and was now finding that she really wanted to change and was building up the inner strength to do so. We focused on the specific danger times, these being when she was at home watching television, feeling guilty for not doing anything constructive or after work when she felt tired and fed up.

We did some further anchoring of positive feelings that would be helpful for her at those times, focusing on changing guilt to a healthier acceptance of relaxation and contentment. As Anna described her hurt and loneliness, she seemed to have greater honesty in her sharing, talking from a deeper place within her. But to be frank I wasn't surprised when she failed to show up to the next session. When I rang her she said 'Oh yeah, I'd forgotten about our session.' I reminded her that she had to pay for the session in any event and from there, I sensed that our time together was now over. And it was. We had six scheduled sessions (including the final one that she had not attended): the first she had been late; the second she had come with no money and had to pay later; the third I allowed her to change at short notice (in an attempt to build a relationship) and after the fourth and fifth, where she had shared more of herself, she had forgotten to come, implying on the phone that it didn't matter.

I hoped that our time together had made a difference in some way, but I was left with the knowledge that I would never know the end of this particular story.

Tom: In the processing, Sandra addresses how Anna can be without her bulimic behaviour, showing how positive 'future pacing' can be used. This exploration into a client's future thinking can often tell us where they really think therapy is heading and of what they are moving away from and towards (a world of potential possibilities).

However, as we see, Anna chooses to disconnect following on from this session, returning to her probably well-versed way of dealing with closeness, relationships and intimacy by detaching from Sandra and the therapy.

It is true that often we never see the long-term effects of our work but we can hope that we have made a difference in some way. It is worth remembering that this could have been the catalyst for a new and nourishing way of being for Anna, or at least opened her up to the possibility of thinking and feeling differently about eating and about what she wanted out of life. If this was the case then Sandra offered her something new, and this was probably enough for Anna at that moment in time.

Hypnohealing (Sandra)

> *The mind is everything. What you think you become.*
> Siddhartha Gautama

Hypnohealing is a very effective but simple way of aiding physical healing via the use of hypnotic visualisations and suggestions. It is founded upon the belief that our thinking affects our physical being and that our thoughts and images can harm us physically and they can heal us. We are talking here about the mind–body connection.

There have been countless studies and research, culminating in numerous books into the mind–body relation, from the masterful work of Erickson, *Healing in Hypnosis* (1984), Erickson, Rossi and O'Ryan, *Mind–Body Communication in Hypnosis* (1986) and Cheek and Rossi, *Mind–Body Therapy: Methods of Ideodynamic Healing in Hypnosis* (1988); to the less empirically led yet often startlingly insightful ideas of Hay, *Heal Your Body* (1982) and *You Can Heal Your Life* (1984), Mason, *Thoughts that Harm, Thoughts that Heal* (2000) and Shapiro, *Your Body Speaks Your Mind* (2005), to name but a few.

For centuries Eastern philosophy has appreciated the continual communication and relationship between the mind and the body. In essence, the condition of the mind affects the body and, likewise, the state of the body affects the mind. Chinese medicine refers to *Jing-Shen*, where it is believed that when the mind is strong, the body will be in good health. The Zen school of Buddhism teaches meditation, where the mind is brought into a sense of harmony with the body – a natural symbiosis of the two.

In Western culture, the medicalisation of the body, and hence the splitting of the mind and body, has meant that much of the Eastern understanding of the mind–body connection has eluded us.

> *You may not yet be able to bring your unconscious*
> *mind activity into awareness as thoughts, but*
> *it will always be reflected in the body as an*
> *emotion, and of this you can become aware.*
> Eckhart Tolle

Currently, the emergence of psychoneuroimmunology (PNI) offers us a scientific insight into the biological processes that operate to sustain our health. A plethora of information (Schedlowski and Tewes 1999; Daruna 2004; Ader 2006; Kendall-Tackett 2009) is on offer to support and clarify what Eastern philosophy has known for thousands of years: that our thoughts affect our bodily reactions. In short, if you think you are ill or sick, then your body can produce the symptoms that correlate directly to your thoughts or if you are frustrated and stressed about something in your life, the body can convert this into something physical (an illness or injury) for you to attend to.

> *A wise man should consider that health is the*
> *greatest of human blessings, and learn how by his*
> *own thought to derive benefit from his illnesses.*
> Hippocrates

The technique starts with the client being directed to turn their eyes inwards and imagine they are going on a journey inside their body, moving slowly down until they reach the part(s) where they are experiencing the unwanted physical symptoms or pain. Once they have indicated they are there, we invite them to describe the area in detail, gaining as much of their sensory experience as possible – what they see, hear, feel and sense. Once this image is clear in the client's mind, they are directed to visualise how the area will look when well (implying that it will become well), describing this in detail so that the subconscious mind becomes aware of the desired outcome. Finally *in their own words*, the client explores what needs to happen to change what they are experiencing in that area to become a healthy, fully functioning image of wellness; symbolically creating the process of healing and inviting the subconscious mind to carry this out.

For example, if a client is suffering from arthritis, they may describe dripping oil over the joints or affected area; cancerous tumours may be eaten away by an army of killer ants; migraines may be soothed by a cold stream of water running around the head; or a 'frozen' shoulder may require a camp fire to be lit underneath it. Clients suggest just these types of visualisations through the creativity of their imaginations, and it is this *excitement* of the imagination that encourages the powerful subconscious mind to begin its healing.

Hypnohealing looks to tap into the deep subconscious mind and stimulate the natural healing resources that are already present and in action in our everyday lives.

The following session of hypnohealing unravels this process with a client with irritable bowel syndrome (IBS).

Working with Irritable Bowel Syndrome

The Client's Presenting Problem

Rachel, 23 years old, presented with IBS wanting help to control the symptoms and the stress and anxiety that inevitably precipitated the attacks. She highlighted in our initial meeting a fear of vomiting and of the symptoms of IBS occurring at difficult moments, such as being in a lecture at university or socialising with friends. Rachel had experienced two bouts of a stomach virus over a period of a month two years previously, which took some time to recover from both physically and emotionally. Three months ago another stomach condition arose and she had since been diagnosed with IBS. The symptoms had been very uncomfortable and led her to being almost housebound and at the point where she could not vary her diet for fear of the consequences.

> **Tom:** I have worked with IBS clients on many occasions and although there is often a complex set of symptoms, these individuals respond extremely well to hypnotherapy, partly due to the nature of the complaint being linked so powerfully to high levels of anxiety. It was no surprise to read that Rachel described a fear of vomiting. Nearly all of the clients I have seen with IBS have described the same feeling, as well as a fear of eating in public: a painful stomach after eating followed by feelings of nausea and concerned people asking 'Are you okay?' as your face turns green. An experience worth avoiding!

It is generally considered that IBS is affected by a client's emotional/psychological well-being. Stress and anxiety are often triggers for the painful and debilitating symptoms to manifest. Often the client feels angry, frustrated and fearful at what they are experiencing, creating further worry and anxiety, which in turn creates further symptoms; a truly vicious circle. I have found that clients with IBS benefit greatly from relaxation techniques, as by focusing on learning to relax the tense areas of the body the attacks ease, and by gaining confidence in taking control of the symptoms, clients can slow down the cycle. Combine this with positive self-confidence suggestions and the client usually experiences a vast improvement in their condition.

I believe it is also essential for the client to explore the 'stressor' (what causes the stress-related symptoms). Stress is often about not feeling able to meet the demands of a situation in the way that they or others expect, and so irrational and limiting beliefs are often at work. SWISH, anchoring, theatre screen and the clenched fist techniques can all help to empower the client in these stress-inducing situations, challenging mistaken beliefs such as 'I'm not good enough' or 'I must not make a mistake'.

It may also be necessary (and it usually is) to explore the first time the symptoms occurred via regression or hypnoanalysis, with the aim of looking for the meaning of the symptoms and the limiting, but universal and protective, learning taken from the original experience. Once the originating event is worked through and understood there is often no longer any need for the symptoms to be present.

Choosing the Technique

This was Rachel's second session. During the first session she told me of her experience of IBS, explaining that she did not feel particularly stressed, only anxious about going out in public, vomiting and stomach pains, all in fact relating to the IBS. She did not seem to hear how stressed she sounded when describing 'being ill'; having suffered little illness in her life this was a new and shocking experience for her.

In the first session I focused on teaching her relaxation techniques and building up an artfully vague 'special place' in her mind, with some suggestions thinking (her primary modality was auditory digital) about her mind and body beginning to work smoothly and in harmony. I finished with her imagining being just the way she wanted to be, using the words that she had described in the exploration phase (freedom, confidence and peacefulness).

This hypnotic intervention had led her to tears as she described how bad she had actually been feeling, pouring out all the things that worried her (the way she envisioned her future being a prominent theme). As Rachel came to a realisation and acceptance of just how distressed she felt, there was a need to begin working on the IBS symptoms specifically, combined with the emotional/psychological meaning of them. So, in the second session I wanted to encourage some healing of the precise IBS areas, teaching her a symbolic way of easing symptoms when they arose, alongside long-term healing of the problem area. Hypnohealing was the natural intervention here.

> **Tom:** As Sandra suggests, the cycle of pain, stress, anxiety and thus heightened pain is *so* frustrating for someone with IBS that they often become consumed by it. Cycles like this are hard to break but hypnohealing is a great tool to help Rachel begin to do this.
>
> In the first session Rachel was moved to tears at the end of the hypnosis which reminds me of so many clients who have experienced a similar profound sense of relief as their symptoms subside and they recognise just what 'feeling relaxed' is really like for them.

The Session

Sandra: How have things been, Rachel?

Rachel: I have been thinking a lot more about how I am, and how and when the IBS is at its worst.

This is good to hear as Rachel is curious about herself and wanting to know more. For me this is a big step towards self-awareness and empowerment.

Sandra: What have you been learning that's helpful?

Rachel: I always get pain when I eat. I feel very uncomfortable and nauseous and have noticed a bad taste in my mouth. I feel really heavy until it all calms down.

I notice that Rachel seems to be finding it easier to describe how she is feeling physically in this session.

Sandra: So you have had this uncomfortable, heavy feeling and bad taste for *every* meal?

I accentuated 'every' meal to see if this was the case and I picked out words that may have emotional relevance as well. For example, what in her life leaves a bad taste? What emotion is heavy?

Rachel: No. I have had quite a good week really, right up until Friday, and then it turned bad.

Here we can see how the client initially generalised her experience as 'uncomfortable for *every* meal' and now describes it as being a good week until Friday.

Sandra: So it seems that you have good and bad days. Tell me about what makes a good day for you.

Rachel: This is where I feel in control and I am getting things done. (Silence.) Take today, I've had a good day because I have really got down to making a start on my essay. I've also been out for a run and done some jobs. A bad day is when I feel restless, tired and confused. I feel stressed, nervous and anxious.

She returns to talking about the bad day so I follow this.

Sandra: So on the bad day you feel restless, tired, confused, stressed, nervous and anxious.

I wanted Rachel to hear what she had said to take her into the felt experience, inviting her to describe further what it was like for her. Connections and meanings can often be made when time and space is given to the experience and words used to describe it.

Rachel: Yes. I also feel disorganised and unhappy.

Sandra: Can you give me an example of this from last week?

Rachel: Yeah, Friday I had a particular lecture in the morning, one that I haven't felt well enough in the past to attend and I felt really unsettled about going. I've missed a lot of the work and I don't really know what to expect or where everyone is at. When I woke up and thought about going to the lecture, I felt really nervous and anxious about it. I know I need to go because there is an attendance criteria, but in the end I had such a bad stomach that I couldn't go.

In this session Rachel had mentioned her university course twice (doing her essay and attending lectures) and I am wondering how she really feels about her course/degree or what it is about this particular lecture that has caused the nervousness. I note that for her it seems as if the physical symptoms come first and then stop her doing things, but I wonder about it being the other way round.

Sandra: It seems you felt unsettled about the day and then became unsettled in the stomach.

I want to see how the client responds to my tentative connection.

Rachel: I guess so. It took me a couple of days really to get over it, now I think about it. That makes me think there was just the one bad day, but my body needed time to recover. It goes right to my stomach and my intestines. (She begins to describe in greater detail.)

Sandra: How is this particular lecture for you?

Rachel: I haven't been to many of them and so I feel very disorganised in the subject. I am confused about it really. I'm worried now as I will have some coursework to do on this and I don't really know where to start.

Sandra: You sound like you really are conscientious in your studies. As I imagine what it might be like being you, I feel that your studies are very important.

Rachel's eyes well up with tears.

Rachel: Goodness yes. I really want to do well. I have set myself a goal of getting a 1st or a 2.1. I *so* want to get a good degree.

I could have continued exploring the core beliefs regarding education, intelligence or Rachel's expectations of herself, but at this stage (session two), I felt it was more important to explore the links between the emotional and physical realms and begin some healing work with Rachel. She had never had therapy before so timing and pacing the work appropriately was important.

Sandra: I am wondering if the pressure to do well, and the worry that you might not, are linked to the physical symptoms that you experience. Do you have any thoughts (auditory digital) about that?

Rachel again became tearful.

Rachel: I do really want to do well and I worry that I'm not going to pass. I certainly feel much better when I'm working hard and studying, getting things done. I hadn't really thought about the link like that before. I had put the symptoms first and seen them as stopping me from doing things.

Sandra: And the tears?

Rachel: I *really* want to do well. I have set my heart on it. It's such a worry for me.

I felt a deep sense of needing to do well. We held the silence, sharing what felt like a brief moment of connection.

> **Tom:** In this session we see how Sandra directs the exploration to Rachel as a 'whole being' and not just the IBS. This helped her begin to be curious about her experiences, focusing on the comfortable rather than the uncomfortable days at first and then the discomfort that Rachel experienced during the week.
>
> In breaking down these experiences Rachel considers the order of events, incorporating the onset of her symptoms – that is how her physical responses are preceded by unsettled feelings.
>
> Rachel also begins to open up to the possibility that her symptoms are accentuated by the different stressful situations she experiences, such as her learning and achieving.

Sandra: It may be useful to come back to this in another session, but I'm thinking that now it would be helpful to show you a technique that you can use to lessen the IBS symptoms. By working on both – what causes your stress in a future session *and* also by healing the area now – this can make a real difference for you.

Rachel: Yes, that would be great.

Sandra: So we are going to tap into something that the subconscious already does very well. That is physical healing. The subconscious already does a very good job of mending broken bones or torn muscles as you know. (She had experienced both.) So by generating a visualisation of what the troublesome area looks like, together with one of how it should look when well, we can give the subconscious mind something to work towards, reminding it of health and well-being and from there it can find a way of achieving this.

Rachel can relax with the knowledge of what is going to happen and the expectation of change.

Rachel: That sounds good to me.

I proceed with the induction, using a passive progressive relaxation, suggesting that change is inevitable and happens naturally (giving a few examples that she can relate to). I also explain how pain creates muscle tension and discomfort and so by learning how to relax the muscles she can relieve some of the pain.

Sandra: What I would like you to do now is imagine turning your eyes inwards and move them down to the area of concern, and describe it to me.

Rachel: My stomach is soft and red and my intestines greenish and bumpy. It's long and thin and the discomfort is at the end. It's all green, black, thick and bumpy.

Sandra: Just take a closer look now at the end where the discomfort is and describe it to me … What causes the discomfort?

Rachel: There is a blockage … (Silence.) It's green gunk, trapped, but I have no idea why it is blocked.

There was nothing more she seemed able to describe.

Sandra: How does your stomach and intestine look when well and healthy?

Rachel: My stomach should be pink and my intestine clear.

I repeat this back to her to see if there is any more she would like to say.

Sandra: What do you need for your stomach to be pink and for there to be no blockage? (Silence.)

Rachel: I need something to suck out the green gunk from the inside, a hose type thing, and my stomach needs a coat of pink paint.

There is no need to use medical terminology. Allow the client to be as creative as they wish and to describe what works for them. I suggest to Rachel that she imagines the hose and it sucking the green gunk away, and as she does this I suggest she notices relaxation start to flow, with comfort and ease beginning to be part of her experience. When she has cleared her intestine, she takes some pink paint and begins to change the red of her stomach to pink, and again I suggest increasing comfort and calmness with every brushstroke.

Sandra: Is there anything else that needs to be done?

Rachel: There are noises coming from underneath my stomach. It's like bubbles of air just underneath.

Sandra: How would you like it to be?

Rachel: For there to be calmness, no noise, no bubbles.

Sandra: What needs to happen?

Rachel: I'm not sure … I don't know … I just want it to be normal.

Rachel seems to be struggling with this part and so I decide to guide her a little. In hindsight the bubbles needed further exploration perhaps before her mind would allow us to know what was needed.

Sandra: I want you to focus your mind on the bubbles and the noise, hear them and feel them. And as you hear them and feel them, you imagine those bubbles beginning to calm and settle just like a fizzy drink going gently flat, and as you watch them calm and settle, a sense of stillness begins to occur. How is that?

Rachel: That is much better, yes, the bubbles are settling.

Sandra: That's good. And you can imagine the bubbles continuing to settle with every breath that you breathe … gently easing and calming. And you can imagine every day from now on, cleaning and clearing the tubes and painting your stomach pink, allowing your mind and body to work as it naturally wants to and has done before … in harmony, feeling a sense of well-being and a sense of health and wellness. And when you are ready, in your own time and in your own way you can gently open your eyes, coming back to the room.

Tom: Sandra describes the hypnohealing visualisation by encouraging Rachel to explore what she sees inside her and how she thinks this should look when well. As Rachel turns her stomach pink with the help of pink paint, she then notes the bubbles underneath her stomach, which she does not seem to know what to do with. Sandra uses pure suggestion to calm and settle the bubbles, which was effective.

However, I found myself wondering over the times I have soaked in the bath surrounded by bubbles, and then picked up the soap to wash, only to be disappointed that the bubbles began to disappear. I wondered whether Rachel could cover the bubbles with soap so that they would disappear or perhaps she could turn on a wind machine (the one just under her stomach) to blow the bubbles away. There are countless other ways that the bubbles could be dealt with showing how immensely creative our imagination can be.

I was also left wondering what the bubbles meant, as they were unexplored initially, and seemingly a sticking point in the hypnotic intervention for Rachel.

Rachel opened her eyes and I waited for her to be fully present, quietly exploring my own thoughts and feelings. She looked younger than her years, 15 or 16 maybe; confused, scared and very unsure of herself. I wanted to tell her 'it will be okay' and reassure her, yet I had a sense this would be un-therapeutic and unhelpful for Rachel, and for my benefit only. However, these thoughts did allow me to attune to how vulnerable and fragile Rachel seemed, and I sensed there was more to her than she was able to put into words right now.

She still said nothing and it felt right for me to ask, 'How are you?'

Rachel: That was really good. Thank you. (Tears began to fall.) I kept thinking about when I was ill two years before and all the decisions I had to make in my life. It has taken me back … it was such a time of uncertainty, instability and I was so unsure of myself.

Sandra: Maybe in our next session we can explore this time, as it seems your mind is showing us what is important for you.

Rachel: I'm shocked, but yes, I think that would be helpful, as from then on I have really struggled.

Sandra: In the meantime perhaps you would like to practise the visualisation each day?

Rachel: I will … thank you.

Tom: As I read the processing of the session, I have a real sense of Rachel's younger self and even find myself wanting to reassure her. Sandra worked well with this, not falling into rescuing and reassuring, but offering her warmth and empathy when it felt the right time to do so.

The Processing of the Session

Rachel initially presented as someone who wanted to combat her IBS, viewing this as separate from herself and her other life worries, but by the end of this session, she was beginning to connect with more than just her physical world. I could sense a fear and confusion that she dare not put into words. Here, the technique was effective but more importantly the session brought into her awareness the fact that her mind kept leading her to the traumatic experience of being very ill with food poisoning (*Salmonella*).

What Happened Next?

The next few sessions explored this illness (using hypnoanalysis) and the decisions Rachel was making in her life at the time. With this she began to link the present-day causes of her stress and IBS with her past. I learned how she felt 'dumb' in her family and thus beholden to gain a 'good' degree. In each session we incorporated various visualisations that focused her on how she wanted to be and what this would be like (e.g. the miracle day).

We progressed through five further sessions before she decided that she needed time to put to good use all the knowledge and techniques that she had learnt throughout our work. Her IBS symptoms had greatly reduced and she was trying different foods and gaining confidence in going out and about. Rachel was well on her way.

Tom: This session prepared a sound basis for the future work that followed and allowed Rachel to explore areas that were likely to approach the core of her anxiety, such as the high expectations she had accepted as her own. Usually these stressors lay at the root of IBS, and this exploration was a central focus to the work with Rachel and one which created the change that she was looking for.

Therapy ended for Rachel when she had learnt more about herself and her symptoms had eased, allowing her to get on with her life as she wanted. There is of course the potential for more work to be done, as I think Rachel has only just scratched the surface of things, but for her, life became easier and her goals for therapy were achieved.

Chapter 4

The Art of Analytical Work

Regression Therapy (Tom)

> *Forgiving does not erase the bitter past.*
> *A healed memory is not a deleted memory.*
> *Instead, forgiving what we cannot forget creates*
> *a new way to remember. We change the memory*
> *of our past into a hope for our future.*
> Lewis B. Smedes

We all regress at some point or another to a younger version of ourselves. It can happen in a heated conversation when we don't feel heard, when we are alone thinking about a troubling situation or even on a bus when we see somebody who reminds us of someone from the past. All of these situations and many more are able to change our experiencing of time, moving us out of the 'here and now' and back into our past.

Think for a moment about a time when you felt chastised or 'told off' at work. In this scenario, it is not uncommon to see grown adults become childlike in their demeanour, as though they have become 5, 6 or 7 years of age, unable to hold on to their emotions, crying or ranting uncontrollably. Indeed, as therapists we are often asked to help in situations like these so that a more adult and confident state can be held, stopping the powerful emotional experiences from unleashing themselves.

Even when we are congratulated for an outstanding achievement, the praise received can make us feel much younger than we are and cause us to blush self-consciously from embarrassment. I am reminded of being at my master's degree ceremony: my mother straightening my tie and cleaning the lunch I had just eaten from around my mouth with the handkerchief she had just licked. I didn't feel very 'grown up'!

When clients are describing experiences from their past I often watch them as their body language becomes foetal – tucking their legs up underneath them, their voice sounding younger and their facial expressions and muscle tone somehow taking years off them.

> *How old would you be if you didn't*
> *know how old you are?*
> Satchel Paige

We generally think of time in terms of our biological age. However, you may be aged 45 in terms of this particular unit of time, but how old do you actually *feel* physically, emotionally, intellectually, mentally and spiritually? If I have worked in a physically strenuous job for many years my well-worn body may feel older than it is biologically. If I didn't learn how to face criticism or disappointment as I grew up, then my emotional response to these situations will likely be that of a much younger age. Conversely, some children, even in their early infancy, seem to carry a certain wisdom about them as if they have been here before, their spiritual sense appearing vastly more developed than their biological age would suggest.

In getting to grips with these experiences of different ages we become better accustomed to the concept of regression – moving back through time to an earlier age and re-experiencing events from that time as if they are happening now. It is in this 're-experiencing' that regression differs from 'remembering'. When we remember something we look back on that experience with a degree of detachment or distance. We may well recall how we felt about the experience at the time, but we do that with our current perspective, from our current age and with a degree of choice as to what parts of the memory we choose to look at (and what not).

In a *regressed* state we move the client through time, back to an earlier age and to a 'problem' time in the past where the client appears 'stuck' in their development. We regress back as though they were there once again; a *revivification* of the original event with all the images, thoughts, feelings and behaviours, just as powerful as they once were. At this stage we see the real power of the mind to hold on to emotional energy that was unable to be expressed at the time.

> *The past is never dead. It's not even past.*
> William Faulkner

In our early years we adapt, and often adapt very well, to learning how we need to be in *our* family life. For example, sometimes we learn that anger is beaten down or tears are swiftly scolded until they dry up, and with no outlet these emotions get locked away. This shutting down of our feelings could be for any emotion: anger, sadness, hurt, guilt, shame, fear, happiness or joy. These feelings all hold an equally valuable place within us, and are therefore all capable of being repressed, only to re-emerge years later through thoughts, feelings and behaviours that we struggle to make sense of and control.

How often have you been driving your car and seen another driver screaming and shouting, writhing in their seat like a crazed wounded animal fighting for its life, and all because another driver failed to indicate correctly or pulled out of a turning in front of them just a little too late? How much of this anger is relative to the situation and how much is from stored up and repressed material, looking for an apparent bona-fide reason to be let loose and expressed?

> *Memory is the diary that we all carry about with us.*
> Oscar Wilde

Regression allows us to revisit these past experiences and re-experience not only the memory, but also the powerful emotions that were present at the time, and which were suppressed due to the lack of an acceptable outlet. In doing this we enable the client to unlock the emotional charge and hence unblock the psyche. In regressing to an earlier time it is not uncommon for clients to sob with sadness or scream in anger with the unabated intensity of a child. Bearing witness to this release of emotion can be a powerful experience. However, the abreaction and catharsis that occurs from this release is remarkable, as afterwards the client's demeanour, facial expression and overall 'feel' changes before your eyes, as a part of them moves from the past into the present and 'grows up', so that they can think, feel and behave more from the here and now, with additional choices and greater wisdom.

In hypnotic regression therapy, there are an infinite number of ways to guide the client back to their past, limited only by the imagination. In the arm raise regression method, by lifting the client's arm in the air we re-create an earlier childhood experience – perhaps of holding a hand up in the air in the school classroom, or being dragged around the shops at breakneck speed or even being a baby crying in the cot and reaching up for their mother. This method doesn't direct us to any specific age, but relies on the client's subconscious mind to regress them back to a past event that requires exploration.

To search for a more specific time, where the age of a trauma is known, we can regress the client to that event and the associated emotions using methods such as a screen regression, where we direct our client to rewind the movie of their life on a screen in front of them, from the present back to moments just before the 'event', or we can guide them down a street, viewing the numbers of each door getting lower until we reach the age in question, when we enter the house and all the thoughts and feelings stored away there. Simpler techniques, such as the affect bridge (Watkins 1971) involve simply suggesting to the client that as we count back from ten to one that with each count they are becoming smaller and younger until we reach number one, where they will be *in* the event that requires exploring.

One of our favourite methods is the library regression technique, where a client is directed to an imaginary library in their mind where they begin to explore the many books that surround them; in particular, a set of books with a number on each spine that relates specifically to each year of their life. First, we guide the client to the book that denotes all that is happening in their present life, suggesting they take the book with the number of their current age off the shelf and exploring what they find as they open it. In setting up the exploration of their *current* life experiences we give ourselves a place to return to when our hypnosis is nearing its end, and in so doing we safely aid a re-orienting back into their present age, when needed.

At this point we direct the client to put the book back on the shelf and move down through the numbers on each volume, each one relative to a year of their life, until we get to the age we want to explore. Then we take that book off the shelf, open it and explore what the client reads, sees, hears or senses inside. Once we have examined the contents of the book we can move even further down through the volumes to an even earlier age and repeat the process, several times if necessary.

This method offers a way of uncovering the repressed emotions connected to the presenting problem. The client can be guided to a specific number where a known event is positioned or we can suggest that the client's subconscious mind will choose the book that needs exploring, making it a versatile method of being direct and indirect with our guiding of the client's experience.

Once we have explored the chosen segments of the client's life, we then return to the first book, of their present age, where we ask them again to tell us what they find as they open the volume. This begins to bring their awareness back to the here and now, and once we have put the book back on the shelf we then leave the library, directing the client back into the room where they can then analyse the experience.

Let's see this technique in action.

Gagging

The Client's Presenting Problem

Antoine presented to me one hot August afternoon in my London office. I recall the afternoon in particular as the recent smoking ban had driven 90 per cent of the bar opposite my therapy room outside, and the noise was becoming distractingly louder as the evening dawned and drinkers congregated.

My first impression of Antoine, a young man of 21, was that he appeared agitated and nervous. Although many clients appear anxious in the first few sessions, Antoine seemed to be more jumpy than was usual. As we began to engage, he explained that his problem was gagging which he had suffered from for as long as he could remember. What was a little different on this occasion was that Antoine reacted so badly whenever something came near his neck that he would be physically sick. I have treated quite a few clients with the same presenting problem, but for a client to gag to this degree was remarkable in my experience. Antoine explained further that if he wore a shirt that was too tight around his neck or if his iPod leads got tangled then the same gagging reflex would also occur.

Antoine told me that the main reason he had decided to seek therapy was that dental treatment was becoming almost impossible as every time the dentist approached his mouth he would begin to gag violently and, on occasions, vomit (much to the annoyance of the dentist). Antoine began to gag while he was telling me about the last occasion at his dentist and I was, in truth, taken aback by the severity of his reaction, asking somewhat nervously whether this was going to happen *now*, which seemed to allow him to bring the reflex back under control.

Born in southern France into a big family, he recalled playing on the beaches near his home around the age of 8, gagging and then running home, scared by what he was experiencing. Before that time his memory was sketchy and mainly concerned with general family life.

During the next two sessions I worked with Antoine, teaching him methods for controlling his thoughts of potential gagging and showing him how this affected his behaviour. I taught him a classic anchoring technique and also worked on lowering his overall anxiety through relaxation and ego-strengthening methods. However, after the third session, Antoine reported that the gagging reflex was still in full force and said it felt like something was 'stuck'. I sensed that there was indeed much more in this simple statement than appeared to Antoine, so I waited, saying very little and feeling lost and a bit stuck myself.

He continued by reminiscing about his time in France and how he missed the days of sunshine and living by the beach. He remembered a few occasions before the age of 8 where he recalled being at parties, being out with his family or at school, and he was surprised when he realised that he could not recall gagging on any of these occasions. These reflections on his childhood led me to feel that an exploration of his past may be useful and I suggested that perhaps we could use regression in hypnosis to explore the earlier years of his life before the gagging started. He was keen to proceed.

Sandra: Tom's matter of fact 'practical' question during the initial meeting. 'Are you going to vomit *now*?' made me smile. I imagine Tom thinking about witnessing this and then having to clear it up. Therapists are only human! Clients bringing the experience into the room really can have its drawbacks at times.

After three sessions, there is clearly no change in the symptoms, so in the next session there are two people in the room – neither of them knowing what to do next, both experiencing being stuck and hoping the other will rescue the situation – mirroring the story that Antoine later tells. So often the process between therapist and client reflects something meaningful.

In session four, Antoine shares some of his childhood memories and together with the analytical mind of this client, who keeps wondering why he cannot remember gagging as a child and yet feeling he had been doing this all his life, regression seems a natural way forward.

Although I agree that regression or hypnoanalysis emerges at this point as the intervention of choice, I ask myself why Tom chose specifically the library regression technique. This isn't hard to answer: if we imagine doing a regression technique that starts with the symptoms then Antoine would be gagging and vomiting within seconds! The library regression is a technique that avoids direct exposure to the cause. It also allows the client to become familiar with being in a regressed state, and gives the therapist control and the ability to move on from material not deemed relevant to the presenting problem or the session's focus. It allows for issues to be explored safely and at depth by turning the pages of the book, or when necessary by closing the book.

The Session

I induced hypnosis using the classical Elman (1984) method, a favourite of mine for inducing a good quality and depth of hypnotic trance. Once in hypnosis I asked Antoine to imagine being 'transported' to an old house, where he was to find himself standing at the front door of the building and about to enter. This set the scene for the journey into the past and we proceeded with the session.

Tom: And I want you to imagine now the door in front of you, and tell me what colour the door is.

This question was designed to check that Antoine had associated into the imagery so we could proceed further.

Antoine: Oak, dark oak.

Tom: Good. Now, I want you to imagine walking into the old house, and as you look around, notice the different doors leading off into various rooms … and then notice one door, just one door in particular that seems to beckon you towards it … and as you begin to walk towards that door you can notice that there is a word written on the door, which informs you that this is the library of the house. I want you to open the door and walk inside … (Pause.) Once inside you can notice the books … many, many books. And you begin to wander around the library now and begin to explore all of these books, all of different sizes and colours, some old and some new, and as you do so, very soon you begin to notice a particular set of books that seem to attract you towards them … and you begin to walk towards those books … and as you get nearer to those books you notice the colour of them, and tell me what colour the set of books are, Antoine.

Again, I ask him about the colour of the books to check his association into this part of the imagery.

Antoine: Red.

Tom: Excellent, and now you can also begin to notice that written down the side of those books is your name, Antoine, and that also written on each book is a number, each book and each number relating to each year of your life, starting from your present age right the way down to number one, the first year of your life. And so I want you to go to the book with the number of your present age on it. And tell me what number that is.

It is vital that there is a base-line exploration, the present day, before tracing back to the specific regressed age. This creates a 'present-day' place of safety to go to at any stage of the regression, and especially at the end, so that the client is not left in a regressed state.

Antoine: 21. (His present age.)

Tom: Excellent. (Positive reinforcement that he is doing this correctly.) And I want you to take that book off the shelf and open it to the first page and tell me what you have there.

Antoine: It's me at work, looking bored. (He sighs and his face looks bored!)

Tom: Okay, and now turn to the next page and tell me what comes next.

Antoine: And now I'm home in France, with my cousins. (He smiles. He had been back to France recently, where his gagging had become worse.)

It is very important to take the client gradually through the process and so after having created this solid image of the 'now', we could begin to move to an earlier time.

Tom: And now, Antoine, I want you to put that book back on the shelf. And then I want you to begin to follow the books down, number by number, until you get to the next book that you seem attracted towards and … tell me, what number is on that book?

Antoine: It's 14.

Tom: Good … and now take that book off the shelf and then open it to the first page, and tell me what you have there.

Antoine: I'm at school. I don't like it here. (Antoine looks angry.)

Tom: And tell me what's happening there.

Antoine: I'm in class and I'm sitting near the window. I hate it here. I just want to be at home. People are so cruel and I just don't want to be here any more.

We began to explore this experience at school. While he is visibly upset and angry I keep in mind that he has been gagging long before the age of 14. I have two choices at this point: to stay with this experience and work through it or continue to an earlier time in his life when the gagging started. I choose to go back further, with the awareness that it would be possible to process the 'school experience' at the end of this session or during a subsequent session.

Tom: And now, Antoine, you can close that book and put it back on the shelf, knowing that you can come back to that at another time. And when you have done that, begin to move again down through the numbers, just moving down through the numbers until you get to the next one that is *important to us today*. (Change in tone so as to engage the subconscious in the importance of this suggestion and the session focus.) And then tell me what number that is.

Here I attempt to relate the regression back to gagging and he picks book number 6 and opens it.

Antoine: I'm 6. I'm playing with my cousins. We're running around near the garages. We usually play around here and it's really good. Michel and Nicolas are daring me to jump off the garage and it's really high. They are better at jumping than me.

Tom: And what happens then?

Antoine: I do it. (He smiles.)

Tom: Great … and then Antoine … what happens then? (Moving the experience forward a little.)

Antoine: Now we're running home. Michel and Nicolas are chasing me but I can run really fast! (His tone has notably changed to that of a much younger, excited boy.)

Tom: That's excellent, and what happens then!? (I match Antoine's excitement.)

Antoine: I jump over the fence … and then …

Tom: Go on …

Antoine begins to gag, violently. I calm my own breathing and tell Antoine, 'It's okay … Keep breathing!', realising as the words left my mouth what a daft thing this was to say.

Tom: What's happening, Antoine?

Antoine: Shirt … on fence … round … neck … (He chokes.) Can't breathe … shirt caught … Dizzy … all going fuzzy and cold … black …

At this stage Antoine slumps and I freeze. What feels like moments pass by and then I tell Antoine, 'Keep breathing *now*, Antoine.' Antoine then takes one almighty gasp for breath and then tears begin to stream down his face as he leans forward, holds his head in his hands and sobs. I just sit … and wait. Two to three minutes later, which seemed like an eternity, Antoine begins to breathe more normally.

> **Sandra:** When we enter the 6-year-old's world there is a wonderful sense of freedom, fun and confidence in his abilities (to run at least), which seem lost to him at 21.
>
> As the scene is revealed and Antoine begins to choke, Tom remains outwardly calm, holding the intensity of the moment. Backing away from this (by turning the pages or closing the book) could have closed the emotional expression and potentially left Antoine overwhelmed. Tom has a moment of panic (mirroring his client's experience). I am sure that we would all feel that way with a client choking and possibly about to black out. Tom's words 'Keep breathing', which in hindsight he questions, is probably something that Antoine's cousins would have said at that very moment. How would we react when Antoine appears to have stopped breathing in the session? Shake him, shout at him or run out of the room for help?
>
> Tom holds his nerve; he alerts the client, addressing him directly and suggesting the present (now), commanding him to 'Keep breathing *now*, Antoine.' This holds the client in the experience but also keeps him physically safe, moving him gently towards the emotional catharsis.

Tom: Just keep breathing now, Antoine … and what's happening now?

Antoine: My cousins … they … they saved me. My shirt, it got caught on the fence as I climbed and jumped over, and it went around my neck. I was hanging there choking and I was so scared. Then everything went black and I passed out. I don't know how long I was there but all I remember next is Michel and Nicolas holding me and lifting me up. I was choking. (Antoine begins to cry again as the emotion takes over. He puts his face in his hands.) How could I not have remembered that? I don't know. That's just how I feel when I'm gagging! (He says this with a feeling of shock and surprise.)

> **Sandra:** Tom is a gentle, silent witness for the client's abreaction, remaining alongside, in the same space, respectful and yet fully present. He does not reach forward and comfort the client, attempt to rescue him or close the book – all these would have been about his inability to hold Antoine's emotions which could leave him in the trauma and/or thinking that he should not be crying about it. Tom just remains present. The regression though is not yet over and he encourages Antoine to continue to what we assume is his 'rescue' (he is still alive after all). I am touched at the savvy of his quick-thinking friends who save him.

At this stage we have just enough time left to process safely what Antoine has been experiencing, so I decide to bring this part of the session to an end.

Tom: Now I want you to put that book back on the shelf, remembering we can come back to it anytime you wish and want to.

Always make the assumption that the client is still regressed even if they *appear* to be talking in the present, as Antoine does, in the final part of his dialogue.

Tom: And as you put that book back on the shelf now, I want you to go back up to the book of your present age and see that number there … (I check he has it. Pause.) And as you do, you can take that book off the shelf and open it to one of the pages you explored before and just notice what comes to you there.

This is designed to begin to bring Antoine back to his present age. He smiles at this stage, and not needing to know why, with a sense that he has moved to his current age, I continue.

Tom: And that's good, and enjoy that smile, Antoine, and you can just keep that experience with you now and then imagine putting that book back on the shelf, and as you do that, then begin to make your way back to the door of the library and then leave, going back out of the house to the outside and then begin to become aware … aware of the chair beneath you, your feet on the floor, and just become aware of the here and now. (Re-associating him back into the present.) And even begin to think maybe of what you are doing later on today. (Again to make sure he comes out of the regressed state to the present.) And then when you are ready, slowly and gently allow your eyes to open.

When Antoine opened his eyes he sat in silence for a while. I chose to do the same, giving him time to re-associate back into the room.

Antoine: Wow! That was just amazing. It was so real, crikes, it was just like it was back then. And the gagging, I can't believe it! All this time, most of my life … I just could never have thought it was due to that.

Tom: And now you have a sense it was?

Antoine: Absolutely. Without doubt. It was that, I just know it.

The session is coming to an end.

Tom: Okay, we are going to need to stop soon, Antoine. I guess this is going to give you lots to think about this week, and it will be good to hear what that is next time.

Antoine: It certainly will, I think. Phew …

After making sure Antoine was fully back in the here and now through talking about his plans for the rest of the day we ended the session and he left.

> **Sandra:** The timing of sessions is crucial and challenging at times. A safe closure out of the regression, making sure the client is fully integrated into his present self and having time for processing the experience is a lot to get through in fifty or sixty minutes. This is certainly something that comes with experience, keeping an eye on the clock and instinct – sensing when and how to move the session on.

As often happens in sessions like this, I sat back down, took a deep breath and smiled. I had real hope that for Antoine this may well be the breakthrough he needed and I was excited to see if this would be so at the next session. I smiled also at the thought that we just never know what is going to happen for our clients in a session, or indeed how we can prepare for unearthing the unknown.

The Processing of the Session

From this session, I came to some understanding of Antoine's lack of confidence. His gagging reflex had hampered him in so many ways throughout his childhood and teenage years, during which he had endured the cruel jibes of his peers. What was important after this session was his way forward. How he lived from now on created the possibility of a whole new experience of the world, one he could now begin to grow within on so many different levels.

What Happened Next?

After a session like this it is hard to plan where to go next. It is likely that the exploration from *this* session would be the focus as well as the impact of the new found understanding of that childhood experience. However, what we plan for the next session often becomes lost once the client turns up! And so what happened next? The phone rang. Antoine was at the other end of the line.

Antoine: Hi Tom. Well, you would not believe. I haven't gagged once, not once for the whole week. I'm waiting for it and it just doesn't happen. It's great. I've even booked the dentist as I've got awful toothache!

Tom: That's wonderful to hear, Antoine. I'm really so pleased. It'll be good to hear about it at our session. (Booked for the day after next.)

Antoine: Well that's just it, Tom, I think I'm OK now. I don't need to come any more. I'm so pleased. I want to thank you so much.

Tom: Antoine, that's great to hear. It might have been good to finish off our sessions with a closure but you know, it really sounds like you have got your own closure, and I guess that's what is really important isn't it?

This begs the question as to what type of closure a therapeutic process should have. I think it is important to consider the purpose of endings and closure. A final session can of course give us a period of reflection with our client, on the past and the future and what has changed, but surely what is most important is what the client needs as an ending and, in Antoine's voice, I simply heard someone rejoicing in a transformational event and wanting to 'be' with it, experience it, treasure it and live it.

In this sense, a final session with Antoine would have been for *my* therapeutic purposes and not for him.

He finished: 'Thank you Tom. This is going to change my life.'

'I think it is Antoine, I think it is,' I said, smiling.

Sessions like this remind me of just how life changing one therapy session can be.

Sandra: It is always a privilege to be a part of such sessions, when the client trusts that you will 'take care' of what they share with you, no matter what it is (known or unknown at the time). They are life-changing encounters for the client and confirm that when you get to the roots and release the client from where a part of them is stuck, results can be quick and effective. Would this outcome have been gained purely by cognitive behavioural hypnotherapy or neurolinguistic programming (NLP)?

Antoine presented with a severe gagging problem. He drew the sessions to a close when his goal had been met and he no longer gagged. He had stopped a behaviour that had been present for most of his life, a part of who he was, which will now take some accommodating.

So although it was an abrupt ending I can understand it. Tom's questioning of it perhaps tells us there is more work for Antoine to do at some point, but not now. I am thinking that in freeing himself from the gagging, he may well be stepping back into being free, playful and confident. He can now meet a younger self without the fear of connecting with his trauma. Thus I imagine that Antoine begins his new found freedom with a sense of the possibilities his future may hold. Quite some life-changing session.

> *Memory is a child walking along a seashore. You*
> *never can tell what small pebble it will pick up*
> *and store away among its treasured things.*
> Pierce Harris

Hypnoanalysis (Tom)

> *Looking back, you realize that a very special person*
> *passed briefly through your life – and it was you.*
> *It is not too late to find that person again.*
> Robert Brault

While regression allows us to open up our clients to the experiences of their childhood, with the aim of gaining clarity of their past and releasing emotional blockages, we are still often faced with the inevitable conflict that a traumatic encounter leaves behind. This is the personal learning that was taken from that time and the unique meaning we make of it, which can remain with us into adulthood. Our past is an intimately private part of our life that no one else can know or hold in quite the same way as us, even though others may have experienced the same events.

Many years ago, I remember a night out with my two brothers, who are six and seven years older than me. After a few casual drinks we got to talking about how life used to be, a reminiscing that was to uncover some startling truths about our recollection of our shared childhood years. 'Do you remember the time in the school holidays when we got into the local school, and the school caretaker was chasing us for ages?' one of my brothers asked. 'Of course', my other brother responded, 'we escaped, but Gary was caught!' 'No he wasn't', I said, 'I got caught!', to which both of my brothers baulked, looking at me in confusion.

'What about that time we got given the hamburger buns by the fairground assistant?', to which one of my brothers exclaimed, 'You didn't get given them, you stole them!', to which my other brother remarked, 'No, they were left at the entrance to be thrown in the garbage!'

Once again we all looked at each other dumbfounded. In fact that night, as we continued to compare stories, we began to wonder if we had grown up in the same house at all, so different were our recollections. Indeed, the time when our mother's priceless antique statue was smashed to pieces during the infamous 'shoe throwing' incident cemented how the same event bore such different versions of the truth for us all.

> *Listen to the mustn'ts, child.*
> *Listen to the don'ts.*
> *Listen to the shouldn'ts, the impossibles, the won'ts.*
> *Listen to the never haves, then listen close to me …*
> *Anything can happen, child. Anything can be.*
> Shel Silverstein

At a young age we don't make sense of our experiences and reactions at an adult, conscious and logical level. We make sense of our world from the age that we are. If I am 3, I have a 3-year-old's developmental stage, vocabulary and logic, which is formed and adapted from someone else's rational logic (our parents' or caregivers' usually). We learn *their* rules which become, in time, part of our reality, our truth and thus part of us; and we use this to make sense of our world. The messages we learn from our parents and caregivers, such as 'Don't get too big for your boots', or 'Who do you think you are young man/lady?' or 'If you are hit, hit back', are adopted as our own as we hear or observe them time and again, eventually forgetting where they came from. We grow up with a whole rule book of how to live, based on somebody else's do's and 'don'ts, and then we live by it.

> *Adults are always asking little kids what*
> *they want to be when they grow up*
> *because they're looking for ideas.*
> Paula Poundstone

While this can remain a satisfactory status quo for many, often we meet clients who have come to a place in life where these messages are questioned or they recognise a pattern that they always follow (for example, choosing abusive partners). 'Why do I always have to do the right thing?', 'Why can't I have fun?', 'Why do I always put others first?', we might ask ourselves, wondering how we seem to be living life on automatic pilot. This, more often than not, takes us back to our childhood, where we first learnt these 'rules', and absorbed the messages that have shaped and moulded our life thus far.

Once our clients have engaged upon this search, they inevitably need to find their own 'truth' and work through any 'unfinished business' from the past. A closure is needed, whatever that might be, and which may on occasion lead to mentally righting the wrongs that have happened to them.

The past has happened and cannot be changed or undone. Yet what can make a powerful difference is helping the adult client build a new relationship with the child part of them that at present is stuck in the past. This child and adult sense of self is evident in the parent, adult and child ego state model written about by Berne (1986). His transactional analysis theory demonstrates how we hold within us our parental and childhood learning (parent and child ego states), as well as an adult ego state that regulates our here-and-now rational understanding of the world. In creating a mental relationship between the adult self and the initially damaged child self, we can begin to heal the wounds that are still present; re-informing and loving the younger part of us that simply needs to understand and feel cared for. This frees the child, bringing him/her into the present as a creatively curious, adventurous and emotionally healthy child.

Have you a sense of your 'inner child'? Let's take you back and see. Become as immersed into this scene as is comfortable, and begin to get in touch with the essence of your inner child.

Breathe deeply and relax now … as we go on a journey to the past … back to your childhood home … and as you stand at the front door, become aware of what you see, hear and feel … and very soon we are going to enter your childhood home as invisible guests … and as you put your hand on the handle … and feel its texture, allow all of those feelings, thoughts and memories to be present … then take a deep breath and enter your childhood home.

As you enter, listen to the sounds … notice whether it's a loud house or a quiet one. Notice any furniture, the carpet and the different doors leading into the various rooms of your childhood home … and as you walk into the living room … it is just as it once was … nothing has changed at all.

And as you look around maybe you find yourself looking now at your father … noticing what he is doing … what he is wearing … and as you look at him, become aware of all those feelings … and then perhaps you look at your mother … noticing what is she doing at the moment … Sense the atmosphere as maybe you become aware of your siblings … brothers … sisters … and what they are doing. And as you do this just become aware of how you feel.

And somewhere in the room you notice … the little you … your child self … and you look at this child very carefully … you look at what the child is doing … and as you look at this young child … you're the only person in the whole world who knows what that child is feeling … the only person in the whole world who knows what that child is thinking … and you are the only person in the world who knows that child's hopes, fears and dreams.

And as you approach that child … your child self … they look up at you and they are the only person in this room that can see you … and you look at their face … and into their eyes … and you know … you understand … and you become aware of all those feelings … as you take the child by the hand and move to the child's room … and look at this room … the furniture … perhaps some toys or books … and you become aware of the atmosphere there.

You hold the hand of the little you as you sit down on their bed … the only person in the world who understands what this child is feeling and thinking and you are the only person in the whole world who knows what that child needs to hear right now … something that maybe nobody has said to the child before … something that the child needs to hear. So you say it to the child, what the little you wants to hear right now. And as you say that you might even want to give the little you a hug … and as you hold that child in your arms … become aware of your feelings. *And then you become the child … held by your adult self … and you look up into your adult self's eyes … and you feel them love you and care for you … and you become aware of those special feelings … savouring that special moment. And once you have savoured that moment, then you become your adult self again.*

You take the child by the hand now and walk out of their room … you pass the mother, father and any other siblings … out into the street … far away to a special place that you know or a place of your imagination, and when you are there ... just allow the child to merge and become part of you ... and know that deep down that child is always there inside you.

And from now on whenever you have thoughts and feelings that your adult self knows are really your inner child's ... all you will need to do is to go inside and tell this child what they need to hear in that moment ... because you are the only person in the whole world who knows what that child needs to hear ... and you might reassure them, play with them or just hold them. You can become a parent to the child ... a parent that child never had but always wanted to have ... you can become a brother ... a sister ... or even a friend to that child.

Now, let your awareness of your current surroundings return fully and be aware of the thoughts and feelings you have experienced on our journey.

Welcome back! Hopefully you have been able to get a sense of your inner child and indeed your relationship with them. What was it like meeting your inner child? Were you able to create a connection with them? In hypnoanalysis work our first goal is to establish for the client a strong, caring relationship with their inner child, so that reparation can occur.

As children we rely on and assume that adults will do the right thing, take charge and make everything alright. We ask them to look after us. Hypnoanalysis looks to create this very experience, where *you*, the adult, become the one who makes the world safe for your inner child. *You* become the adult your inner child looks to when love, care and nurturing are needed. *You* become the adult who looks after the little you inside and explains things, and as it is *you* that becomes this powerful guardian, this nurturing and protective 'inner parent' for the little child inside, that connection will remain there for as long as you live.

The experiences of the past that are still carried inside – when the younger you was disempowered, learned a mistaken lesson or rule and was unable to express how you were feeling – can now be revisited with the adult you alongside your child self, there to speak up for the child, rescue the child, love the child and ulti-mately *re-write* the experience with the child not at fault. For exam-ple, a client comes to therapy believing he/she is clumsy because when he/she was 4, he/she remembers accidentally knocking a glass of water off a table and being severely reprimanded: 'You stupid clumsy girl/boy, what's wrong with you?' In hypnoanalysis, we need the child to understand that he/she was only 4 and that a 4-year-old will naturally have mishaps like this; it is not that he/she is clumsy or stupid. The inner child can then begin to find a sense of personal power, self-acceptance and wholeness, now feeling as important as any other human being (Barnett 1979), its character now given the space to flourish.

In summary, hypnoanalysis is designed to explore the client's internalised ideas of what another 'significant' person in early life thought and felt towards them, or indeed told them.

Our aim is to redress these unhelpful, inaccurate and damaging thoughts, and help our clients to live a life based on what they choose to think and feel today.

> *In every real man a child is hidden that wants to play.*
> Friedrich Nietzsche

A number of important factors need to be taken into account in a session such as this.

1. The work should only be carried out once 'empowering' cognitive and behavioural techniques have been taught to the client so that they can manage the intense feelings that may arise.

2. The client's adult self may not feel or be fully equipped to deal with any internalised aspects of the significant other(s) that created the now mistaken belief (e.g. 'I'm no good'). Hence, as the therapist, we need to be ready to guide them in a safe and supportive way and make appropriate suggestions when needed.

3. There must be an attitude of respect for the client's relationships with these 'others'. If a client didn't get angry when their alcoholic father/mother came home shouting and threatening them, we need to respect this during the session, knowing that at some point later on they may need to be angry.

Let's see how freeing this process is in the session of hypnoanalysis that follows.

Dealing with Weight Issues

The Client's Presenting Problem

I first encountered Sophie around ten years ago when she sought help while recovering from major surgery after a long illness. We engaged in a series of sessions to help her with healing. This time she came wanting to lose weight before her sister's up-and-coming wedding at which she was to be a bridesmaid.

A multitude of prescription drugs over the years had made it seemingly impossible for Sophie to manage her weight gain and an extremely limited diet (due to her previous illness) had proven to be a stumbling block when choosing healthy eating plans. Sophie wanted help to slim down to a size that would enable her to fit into her bridesmaid dress that she had already chosen and was excited about wearing. Her goal was to lose around 56 pounds (approx. 25 kg).

Clients present with weight issues for a variety of different reasons. Some have been overweight for many years and reach a stage where they have had enough; some have gained weight quickly through pregnancy or a change in lifestyle that may be linked to relationship issues or work difficulties; for others it may be they have been told their weight is starting to affect their overall health. While there may be a number of causes behind clients being unable to lose weight and engage in exercise, one of the major problems lies in their thoughts and feelings connected with food.

In all cultures, food has many more purposes than simply giving us the fuel we need to survive. It is used, in family and social settings, as a reward, a punishment or as a way of bringing groups of people together. I have worked with clients who recount childhood stories of being made to eat the previous evening's dinner at breakfast as punishment for not eating it the night before, or being sent to bed without any tea, or clients who have been rewarded with more and more food to mark the 'good' things they have accomplished and achieved – all breeding a powerful connection between food and emotions.

Food plays a vital part in our lives, so it is no wonder that our very existence is closely linked to what and how we feed ourselves (or how we do not feed ourselves in some cases) and because of this, working with clients with eating issues is by no means an easy task.

Having worked with Sophie before, and having seen many clients presenting with some type of eating disorder, I had a sense that we were going to be operating in areas that she would find difficult and challenging. I choose the words 'difficult' and 'challenging' because clients often struggle to appreciate that there is a lot more to overcoming eating issues than they are at first able to realise.

Putting aside medical reasons, such as the side effects of medication or allergies, any dietician will tell us that if we put into our bodies more calories than we burn daily, then weight gain will be the likely result. It may therefore be fair to say that some individuals are blinded from engaging in what is *actually* going on for them in their relationship with food, as initially clients often report that they don't eat unhealthily or that they only eat three meals a day.

It is vitally important to remember when we are working in this area that there are 'out of awareness' strategies being used to keep the client away from the real reason they are overeating – their emotions, their life and their sense of self.

Sandra: I find that some weight loss clients would love a magic wand to wave away their behaviours, allowing them to remain personally untouched themselves.

For those who have a long history of unsuccessful dieting over the years, often with feelings of guilt and low self-worth, remaining untouched in the process of therapy does not usually bring lasting results.

The client's history around weight and early childhood experiences of food, by which present experiences will undoubtedly be influenced, will need examining to explore values and limiting beliefs that have been formed, as these will actively influence the 'now'.

Choosing the Technique

I embarked firstly on a series of cognitive behavioural and NLP approaches to encourage Sophie to take some control of her eating patterns, exercise and self-image. I have found this to be an effective way of starting therapy with clients presenting with weight issues. Firstly, it empowers them with the belief that something *can* be achieved and secondly, it gives them the tools and strength needed to explore the deeper reasons for their continued behaviour. It is in no way easy for anyone to face their early and ongoing connections with food and so helping them to manage their emotions seems not only safe and practical but also empathic and 'human'.

Having begun to help Sophie learn new ways of thinking and feeling, we came to the stage, around five or six sessions later, when we faced the realisation, as she continued to struggle with food, that deeper areas needed to be explored. In one sense it can be terrifying for clients to delve into these matters, as they explore early childhood patterns of reward and punishment, and thus their deeper experience of life. In another sense it can be almost a relief to have permission to accept that there is more to what is happening in and to their body, because the shame and self-blame can be overwhelming.

In the previous session we had discussed Sophie's early years, focusing on her relationship with food and her experiences of mealtimes and eating. She was brought up in a variety of different care homes and recalled sitting at a communal table and being force-fed at mealtimes. On one occasion she recalled her chair being pushed so tightly to the table by one of her carers that the pressure on her body made her physically sick. Indeed, she spoke of many such experiences. Later, when she had returned to live with her mother, she remembered becoming extremely ill to the point where she wasted away to 84 pounds (approx. 40 kg) with Sophie terrified as to what was happening. In these stories I became aware of the polarities in her learnt attitudes towards food. In the care home she was 'fed' up, while later at home she witnessed starvation. One can only wonder at the confusion this would create around food, which is exactly what Sophie described.

These somewhat disturbing stories about eating guided my thinking towards working with her in a re-parenting way. I felt that if the aim for Sophie was to gain a healthy attitude concerning food, it was important to work towards the 'maturing' of the younger part of her that was so enmeshed with confusion and fear around food and eating. This is what led me to discuss and plan with her the following session of hypnoanalysis, during which we could teach her to be a parent to herself and thus give herself the care she now needed.

I initially explored her relationships with her carers in the homes in which she had lived, her mother and other immediate family members. This can be hard for the client (but is important for hypnoanalysis to be effective, open and free) as there is often guilt in talking about family members to 'outsiders' and in admitting that a parent was not resourceful at parenting; this often leaves the client feeling lost and wondering how they survived. However, we are not looking to apportion blame for the cause of our client's difficulties but simply looking to ignite a greater sense of reality and inner care that they can use from this point in life onwards.

Sandra: There is always a need for preparation in analytical work and Tom is mindful of this. There is a need to discuss the impact that 'awareness' could have and how this will be handled when it is gained.

Too often I hear of clients unprepared for new revelations about themselves and significant others in their lives, and then talking with parents straight after a session only to find they deny all knowledge of the experience or become angry and blame the client for how they were as a child. Sometimes the blame is even attributed to the therapist for suggesting such events ever took place.

Please think carefully before your client has any contact outside the therapy room with parents or significant others involved in the work, or what you suggest with regard to how they should deal with their feelings. The resolution *has* to come from within the client.

The Session

Once a good quality of hypnosis was established I continued.

Tom: Very soon I would like to speak to your subconscious mind as if I am speaking to somebody else, and what I want you to do is not to think about my questions, nor consider your answers, and give me the first thing that comes into your mind. So … now, as I count from 1 to 3 and snap my fingers, your subconscious mind will reveal itself as a shape, colour, symbol or image … (1, 2, 3, snap) … Tell me what you have?

Sophie: A purple triangle.

Tom: Excellent, thank you subconscious mind for revealing yourself in this way.

This is so we associate and familiarise the client into the 'concept' of their subconscious mind.

Tom: Subconscious mind, would it be appropriate to go back in safety and comfort to just a few moments before the first feeling or event occurred in Sophie's life that is connected to her relationship with food. Yes or no?

Sophie: Yes.

Tom: Thank you, subconscious mind. And so I am going to count to 3 and snap my fingers and you will find yourself just a few moments before this very first time in Sophie's life … (1, 2, 3, snap) … Are you inside or outside?

Sophie: Inside.

Tom: Is it daytime or night time?

Sophie: Night time.

Tom: Are you alone or is there someone there with you?

Sophie: I'm on my own.

Tom: How old do you feel?

Here I ask how old do you *feel*, and not how old *are* you, so as to engage with the regressed client, not their current logic of how old they actually are.

Sophie: I'm 6.

Tom: What's happening there?

Sophie: I'm sitting on my bed. I've been locked in my room again. I can't eat my tea and they've locked me away again … till I eat it.

Tom: Okay Sophie, it's okay … (I felt reassurance was needed here.) It's night time and you are on your own and you are just 6 years old … and you're in your room sitting on your bed … and they've locked you in there because you can't eat your tea.

Here I ask a few more questions to establish with Sophie an accurate picture of what she has described with as many details as possible.

Tom: And how are you feeling, Sophie?

Sophie: I'm sad and scared. I don't want to be locked away again … (Silence.) It's not fair, I don't like this.

I ask her child self to say more about her feelings and what that is like for her. It is important to remember you are talking to the client's regressed child/younger self, so talk about the feelings involved in the *present* tense, not as if they were remembering something. Also take care to speak to the client's child as if they *are* a child. Be aware of the tone of your voice and the volume of it.

With the event established and the feelings accessed and described, I introduce Sophie's adult self as follows.

Tom: And so, Sophie, I am going to count to 3 and snap my fingers and then your adult self is going to appear in the room with you … (1, 2, 3, snap) … and just see them there now with you … and then on the count of 3 again you are going to *become* your adult self … (1, 2, 3, snap) … And as you have become your adult self … looking at your younger self, you are the only person in the whole world who knows how this little you feels … you are the only person in the whole world who knows how this event has affected this little you … And you are the only person who knows what this little you needs to hear … and so what would you like to say or do now for that little you?

Sophie: I want to go and sit with her. She's so lonely. (Tears began to roll down Sophie's cheeks.)

Tom: And you can just sit on the bed with the little you and just remember that you are the only one who knows how she feels and what she needs right now … and in a moment I'm going to count to 3 and snap my fingers and when I do … I want you to become the little you sitting on the bed with your adult self … (1, 2, 3, snap) … and as you sit there with your adult you, sitting next to you, I wonder what you would like to say to her?

Sophie (child): Why do they do this to me? I don't like it. I really can't eat my tea, I just can't. It's horrid.

Tom: And again as I snap my fingers you become your adult self … (1, 2, 3, snap) … and as you've heard what the little you has said, what do you say back to her?

Sophie (adult): I know, and they *are* wrong. It's not your fault. You are a good girl and I love you very much.

Tom: And become your little self now … (1, 2, 3, snap) … And as you have heard what the grown-up you has said to you, Sophie, what would you like next?

Sophie (child): I want to get out of my room, but I can't. The chair is behind the door. The handle won't move.

Here I realise that a chair has been used to stop the handle being pushed down and so opening the door is impossible. Sophie can't move it. She's only 6.

Tom: Okay, and now as I click my fingers you become your adult self … (1, 2, 3, snap) … and I wonder what you would like to do or say next? (I knew what *I* wanted her to do!)

Sophie (adult): I'm already there. I'm at the door and I'm pushing the handle. She's getting out of here and I'm going to get this door open.

Sophie looks determined. Her face flushes as she works hard … literally. I give her time, and then she screams with elation as she conquers the door and the chair gives way.

Tom: And tell me what's happening, Sophie.

Sophie (adult): I've done it. It's open.

Tom: And now become your little self again … (1, 2, 3, snap) … and what would you like to do now, Sophie?

Sophie (child): I want to go, but I can't, she will hit me. I can't.

I feel tears in my eyes as I hear the fear in her voice.

Tom: And what will help you?

Sophie (child): I need help, I can't do it on my own. She will be so angry.

Tom: And I want you to become your adult self now … (1, 2, 3, snap) … and as you're the only one who knows what the little you needs right now, what do you do?

Sophie (adult): She's coming with me! I'm taking her out now. We're going to walk right the way out. RIGHT NOW!

Tom: And I wonder if there's anything else that you need to do before you leave with the little you?

Sophie (adult): Oh yes! I'm going to find her now. I'm not scared of her … Bitch … We're walking down the stairs now. And … OH … there she is!

Tom: And I want you to keep the 'little you' safely beside you. Hold her tight … and what would you like to say to 'Bitch', Sophie?

Sophie (adult): Who do you think you are?! How dare you treat these little girls like this? How dare you! (I sit trembling in my chair as she shouts loudly.) Now! I'm telling you, if you dare keep locking these girls away for not eating their dinner, NO, in fact for anything, you are going to be very, I MEAN VERY, sorry! … So, I am going now and she's coming with me AND YOU HAD BETTER HAVE A GOOD HARD LOOK AT YOURSELF. DO YOU HEAR ME?

Tom: Does she hear you, Sophie?

Sophie (adult): Too right she does! Standing there looking pathetic. She can only bully children. (Significant for Sophie to realise.)

Tom: And I want you to become the little you now … (1, 2, 3, snap) … and how are you, Sophie?

Sophie: (Sophie smiles and a tear drops from her eye.) I'm happy now. And now I want to go please.

Tom: And now become your adult self ... (1, 2, 3, snap) ... and now Sophie, I want you to take the little you out of that place to another place, to her favourite place perhaps. And when you are there then just let me know. (Sophie nods.)

> **Sandra:** Tom describes a moving hypnotic intervention which allows the client's child 'part' to tell her story, express her feelings and ask the all-encompassing question, 'Why do they do this to *me*?' When I read Sophie's story, I imagine a small child with no stability and trapped by cruelty. Painful, unfair, unjust and experiencing disgusting adult behaviours.
>
> Quite a strong reaction on my part which would, if this was my client, make me aware of the intense anger my client might feel about these times and the impact this has had on her. Consequently she might need to continue further expressing in future sessions as she really has been let down by those who should have looked after her.
>
> Tom gives the adult Sophie the chance to comfort, explain, reassure, rescue and then stand up for the client's 'little' self. It is important to note that it is the adult who expresses the anger and says what she thinks. No one has stood up for the child before and she needed this to happen.

Sophie (adult): Yes, I'm there. We're in the park.

Tom: That's great, Sophie ... and now you might want to give the little you a hug or hold her ... and as you do ... feel her becoming part of you. And from now on you know that whenever you have those unwanted thoughts and feelings about food, it is not your adult self but your inner 'little you' needing you to hear her ... and you can just go inside your mind and tell that part of you what she needs to hear… and maybe give her a hug or just some reassurance that you're here with her to look after her from now on ... Subconscious mind, is there anything else that Sophie needs to explore right now?

Sophie: No.

Tom: Okay, I want to thank you, Sophie, and also your subconscious mind for allowing us to do this important work today and I want you, silently from deep inside your heart and soul, to thank your subconscious mind for looking after you in the best way it has known how, and you can *now* know that you have the ability to listen and hear whatever that little you, ever present within you, wants and needs. And when you are ready now, you can bring yourself back to the here and now, slowly and gently, and when you are ready just let your eyes open, becoming fully alert and aware.

Sophie opened her eyes and started sobbing. My eyes welled up as I experienced the sadness in the room and how it was for the young Sophie. I waited until she looked at me and then she cried some more. When the tears started to subside she looked at me again, smiled, began to giggle and said, 'Boy, she was pretty angry eh!' (referring to her adult self).

'She appeared so', I said, and prompted more from her, 'So what was this like?'

Sophie said, 'I had forgotten how scared I used to be, how the door would be locked. I spent so much time just wishing I was somewhere else. It's almost like everything became a dream. I feel like that now so often, like everything's just not real and I drift off into another place, like I'm escaping.'

'And what happens in that time?' I said. 'Well, that's when I get scared and then I eat, I mean really scoff myself, so I don't have to think about anything. My goodness, I can't believe this is still affecting me!' she replied.

Sophie's last statement was a familiar one after such a session. Once again, it is so important not to assume that clients realise why they are behaving in the way they are. So often this is just simply out of their conscious awareness.

At this stage, nearing the end of the session, my focus moved to how Sophie could manage this realisation, along with the emotions it had brought up. There was a lot for her to reflect on and in the back of my mind I knew it was likely that this would bring up other memories and recollections for her during the week. So we looked at ways for her to contain these thoughts and feelings and settled on her writing them down in her diary so we could explore them at the next session.

We came to the end of the session and as Sophie was leaving I noticed something about her that appeared different. Her face seemed to have changed. She may have even looked just a little older. I noted it and wondered if she felt this as I closed the door behind her.

> **Sandra:** The processing is always so vital in hypnoanalysis. Tom waits and allows the client to describe what happened and where that has taken her, knowing that something will come out of the post-hypnotic exploration.
>
> Here is one of those moments when the client drops from an intellectual to an embodied connection of past and present. If a client comes to us stating that they know why they do something but they still cannot change the behaviour, then they have not reached this level of understanding.
>
> Sophie has realised that she escapes (herself, life), becomes distant, scared and then binges. She can never 'not know' this and will recognise it if/when this next occurs. This session was hugely significant and opened her to a new sense of awareness.

My thoughts turned to my notes and what was important for me to record about the process of our session. Along with the fear, sadness, anger and relief that Sophie appeared to have experienced, she was also surprised at still being affected so long after what she had experienced. I wondered how angry she might now be with me for revealing this to her. I also noted how I felt distant and began to wonder if I was experiencing a 'shutting down' from my feelings, and if Sophie was experiencing this same process.

From our next session onwards, Sophie struggled to engage with me, and I found myself shut out and kept at arm's length. She created a shroud of disruptions in future sessions (talking about arguments at work and with her sister), wanting to only engage and 'battle' on a very intellectual basis and challenging many therapeutic interventions I made. When I reflected this to her she became quite annoyed and antagonistic, and so I changed how I was with her and I waited, patiently, just 'being there'. The session of hypnoanalysis had undoubtedly affected Sophie as she steadily lost the weight she wanted and fitted into the dress for her sister's wedding. The goal she had for therapy was achieved, but it felt as though something was lacking as she continued the sessions.

In the end it seemed to me that there was a point when she realised she could not escape me (Tom), the human being, who was just interested in her (Sophie), the human being; and if she could not escape me, then she could not escape herself; and at that time in her life, she was not ready for this.

Sophie suddenly told me that she had achieved all she wanted and that she was ready to end, and so we did, at her request, at the next session. However, there was a sense for me that her therapy never really ended, it just stopped. I wonder if I will see her again in another ten years time.

Sandra: The ending with Sophie was interesting. Maybe she wanted to leave Tom feeling how she had felt back in her childhood? Or maybe she wanted to treat him in a way that gave her control, where she had none as a child? Or maybe she didn't know how to end at all?

As therapists we need to hold the ending that the client chooses for their own needs at that time. I too wonder if one day Sophie will reconnect with Tom, wanting to explore a little more about herself and her relationships. In knowing yourself comes choice and with choice comes responsibility for yourself, your actions and your life. That takes great courage and a leap of faith, which gives you few places to hide. Maybe Sophie was not yet ready for this aspect of therapy.

Parts Therapy (Tom)

> *I hold a beast, an angel and a madman in me, and*
> *my enquiry is as to their working, and my problem*
> *is their subjugation and victory, downthrow and*
> *upheaval, and my effort is their self-expression.*
> Dylan Thomas

How often have you heard yourself saying, 'A part of me wants to … move jobs, end a relationship, have children, go on holiday, etc.', but another part of me is just too scared, busy, broken or confused?

Maybe sometimes you feel pulled in several different directions, unable to make a choice as to what to do in life, as each tentative decision to move one way feels as though you are betraying another more powerful part of you. This is commonly how we experience the inner parts of our personality in conflict with each other; for some, on a daily basis.

In a typical experience of procrastination, for example, where conflicting ideas, thoughts and feelings exist, we can either talk things through with someone else or we can make a practical pros and cons list to help us clarify what we are thinking. In parts therapy, however, we look to create an *intrapersonal* dialogue between the conflicting personality states (or parts), in order to find out how they are operating with each other and to find which parts have perhaps become more inflated or have too loud a 'voice', and which ones possibly need to be heard more than they currently are.

The concept of working therapeutically with our inner personality states has been used over the years in a variety of different ways. Its early exploration was through one of Freud's followers, Paul Federn (1871–1950), whose work in ego psychology set in motion the concept of the *interplay* of ego parts. This work was popularised in the 1950s by Charles Tebbetts (1913–1992), who coined the term parts therapy and whose work with subconscious personality parts continues to be delivered across the world today by Roy Hunter (2005). Other variations of this approach can be found in

Hal and Sidra Stone's *Embracing Ourselves* (1998), in which they explore creating dialogue between the various selves or subpersonalities. This approach has been written about extensively by John Rowan (1990) and Helen and John Watkins (1997) in their ego states work. Gordon Emmerson's captivating book, *Ego State Therapy* (2007) also describes this process exquisitely.

> *First learn the meaning of what*
> *you say, and then speak.*
> Epictetus

In all of these adaptations, the uncovering of the internal dialogue between parts is the aim. This enables an inner communication, which *most importantly* reveals each of the parts involved, and values them and their role. Very often clients come to therapy wanting to stop being angry, sad, jealous, fearful, shy or whatever emotion or part of them they are judging as 'bad'. Our first task is one of helping the client to recognise that whatever they are feeling, they are feeling for an entirely valid reason. All of our internal voices should hold an equal place within our psyche and have an equal say; all parts have a positive intention behind their words or actions. In therapy, if a client is struggling to move forwards in the way they desire, there is a part that needs exploring that would much rather stay the same. In gaining understanding about the part that would rather stay overweight, keep drinking or being shy, for example, we can find out the positive intentions that part has and work through or meet its needs in a more productive, healthy way.

However, through parental or societal messages from the past we are told that some thoughts and emotions are good and some are bad, and it is this that creates so much angst within us. Parts therapy aims to address the imbalance and help us live life in a fully functioning, free and balanced way.

> *Freedom is the will to be responsible to ourselves.*
> Friedrich Nietzsche

The approach to parts therapy that follows in this session, the meeting room, is an adaptation of the work of David Quigley, who creates an internal dialogue between *predefined* parts of the person-ality, and can be found in his book *Alchemical Hypnotherapy* (1984).

In essence this approach can be adapted in a number of different ways. I have in the past asked my client to imagine they are sitting at the head table of a classroom, and to name and explore each of the different parts that enter the classroom, each of which we may have discussed prior to the visualisation. You can imagine (from your own schooldays) the internalised characters that present themselves; we all remember the bully, the class joker, the brain box or the angry kid, and how a part of us reacted or *wanted* to react to them. This can be adapted further to a scenario of choos-ing members of a team on sports day. What characters were chosen first and last? Think about your own experience of this, the parts it touched within you, and what aspects of you were present in this experience. What part of you got picked first, and what part of you *knew* you would be picked last?

These aspects of you are still carried within, to a lesser or greater degree, and with clients we often see one or more of these parts creating trouble within the psyche. Our job in this approach is simple – conflict resolution.

Let's read how working with personality parts makes a difference for the client in this session.

Shyness and Lack of Confidence

The Client's Presenting Problem

James (25) came to see me presenting with shyness, especially when wanting to ask women out on a date. I have worked with a number of clients struggling to overcome shyness, who complain of blushing, wanting to run away, stuttering or stammering, even finding themselves frozen to the spot and unable to speak. As they are often unable to imagine *not* reacting with these debilitating symptoms, part of our initial work is directed towards their 'self-concept' – allowing them to imagine what life will be like when they are confident and calm in these situations.

During our first session, James explained that in most areas of his life, apart from this one, he was happy. He had a circle of good friends of which many were women and with whom he had healthy flirtatious relationships. However, it was when James became attracted to a woman that he would clam up, finding it almost impossible to speak and inevitably going home wherever he found himself in this situation. He hoped I could help in this *specific* area, stating clearly that he wasn't interested in delving into anything deeper.

During our first three sessions I worked with some degree of success on his shyness, using imagery to enable him to begin to imagine himself reacting differently and responding in the way that he desired. Together, we formulated a number of tasks, including being more confident when asking a woman out on a date. Initially James managed to do this well and produced a variety of reactions from those he approached, ranging from silence to some even saying 'yes'. However, deep down he simply didn't feel comfortable in what he called a 'real' scenario, and which for him our therapy was not addressing.

One of my early observations about James was that his clothing, in our sessions at least, was often dirty and unkempt, his jumpers had holes, his trousers were ripped and his shoes were often untied. I felt that whatever it was that wanted to prevent him from appearing attractive certainly showed in his appearance, suggesting to me that ultimately he would be rejected.

Over three sessions we explored James's different self-perceptions, discussing how and where his anxieties may have started and I began to get a sense that James's 'self-speak', his internal dialogue, was a controlling factor and it was this that we needed to work with.

Sandra: James was certainly looking for specific enlightenment and change, although as is often the case, he could not imagine how that would be. It is time well spent focusing the client towards the possibilities of change and just how good that will feel.

We can also see in these first five sessions or so that Tom was able to build up a picture of the different aspects of his client in operation. Would I have mentioned his rather unkempt appearance in therapy? I think I would have taken an opportunity to do so to find out what this was about. Tom chose not to (I checked) even though, at the end of the case study, he acknowledged this was something that had touched him. I ask myself, 'Is this about me?' James was coming for therapy, not to date Tom! However, I do feel there was, in the way he was presenting, and in Tom's reflections, something meaningful going on. It was certainly incongruent with the 'flirt' part; as later on in the hypnotic intervention this comes across as a little too much considering the way that he presented.

Choosing the Technique

I decided to use parts therapy, as I felt that this could help James recognise which aspects of him were in conflict and also allow him to acknowledge the specific needs of each part of his apparently conflicting personality, aiming to gain some equilibrium and inner communication within the psyche. When one part of our personality becomes over-inflated, or indeed under-nourished, it can influence our behaviour. Parts work aims to redress the balance, giving the client inner awareness and choice, via an 'executive' part. Having explained the process and purpose of parts therapy to James, we progressed with the session.

Sandra: I have many clients who, in our final session, reflect back on the poignant moments in therapy and mention parts work as being the most profound for them, often still imagining the characters that were the inflated parts of themselves.

I remember someone coming to therapy with a social phobia, and in parts work exploring 'the librarian' who constantly sorted out all the information about a situation before the client would be allowed out. Also I remember 'gluttony' for an obese client, who wanted the good life and as much of it as possible, because they remembered what it was like when there was nothing but neglect and abuse.

I have yet to work with a client who doesn't internally shift in some way during parts therapy and, in particular, in an intervention like the meeting room. However, I do not feel that this can be done in the very first few sessions as a level of trust is needed for the client, along with an awareness of and openness to themselves and the conflicting parts that are in operation within their personality.

The Session

During our exploration of the parts of James that seemed to be in conflict, we named and explored briefly: paranoid, shy, lacking in confidence, fun and flirty.

Tom: Okay, in a moment I'm going to begin to create some dialogue between the different parts of you, because the *paranoid, shy* and *lacking in confidence parts* of you seem almost to take over and become all of you, and when that happens, the *fun* and *flirty parts* of you become lost, without a voice.

James: Well, yes, I certainly lose my voice.

Tom: What seems to be happening is that the part of you that is the paranoid you is rejected, and becomes louder than the fun part of you. The reason that the paranoid part of you is louder is something we shall explore as we go through this session. How does that sound?

James: Yes, sounds great to me. I would love to know.

Sandra: This technique brings to light the 'present-day' experience, not looking at the cause but focusing on gaining a greater essence and awareness of what is happening.

With this awareness comes choice. In using metaphors that allow inner negotiations to take place, resolutions for the client's inner self talk (parts) can occur.

Tom: Great, sit back then and begin to relax.

Once James was suitably relaxed in hypnosis, we continued.

Tom: And I want you to imagine now that you are sitting at a table, it is a meeting room table in a large plush meeting room. As you sit at the table, you look around and notice that there are six chairs – six chairs, relating to the six parts of you, one of which you are sitting in … and you are at the head of that table, because at this meeting, *you* are in charge. And so as you look around you notice that there are five other chairs, two on either side of the table and one at the opposite end, and you notice that in each of those chairs are the different parts of you we have been talking about. In one of those chairs is the *paranoid part*, and I want you to tell me where that part is sitting.

James: It's sitting to my right, nearest to me.

Tom: Now notice where the *shy part* is sitting.

James: It's sitting right next to *paranoid*.

Tom: Good, now notice where the *fun part* of you is.

James: Right opposite the *paranoid part* on the other side of the table.

Tom: And where is the *flirt part* of you?

James: That's next to the *fun part*.

Tom: That's good, and finally you notice opposite you on the other side of the table the *lack of confidence part* of you. And so here around the table you have all the different parts of you that are relative to the situation that we have been talking about today.

We now want to explore each part, looking to make each part as present and real as possible in the client's mind. It is important to remember that we are aiming to give each part of the personality a *voice*, as each needs to be heard to create a sense of unity.

Tom: Now I want you to look over at the *paranoid part* and just describe to me how that part looks.

James: (Beginning to smile.) Wow, it's the rabbit out of *Donnie Darko!* (Richard Kelly's 2001 cult psychological-fantasy film.)

Tom: And how do you feel as you see that?

James: Kind of surprised really. When I first saw it, I was scared as I thought it was odd, but mostly surprised.

Tom: OK, that's fine. Now I want you to look over at the *flirt part* of you. What do you notice about that part of you?

James: It looks just like me, but smaller. I think about maybe four foot (1.2 metres). My head can just see over the table.

Tom: Now look over to the *shy part* of you. What is that part of you like?

James: It's just like the *flirt part*. Just the same, like a mirror image. The same size and everything.

Tom: Great, now describe the *lack of confidence part*.

James: That's hard. I can't quite see a face. It's like he's sitting side on … It's almost like he doesn't want to be seen. But he looks just like me also.

Tom: And then the *fun part*.

James: That's just as I see myself.

Tom: That's great, James. Now … what I would like you to do is look behind you, and when you do, you will notice there is a mirror on the wall and in that mirror notice what is there.

This is to get a sense of how the client sees their 'self-concept'.

James: I can't see anything.

Tom: And what's that like?

James: It's hard to explain … I can see the mirror but no reflection. No, no … I am beginning to see myself, but I don't get an impression. I mean I don't *feel* anything.

Tom: It almost sounds like you're not getting a sense of being inside yourself.

James: Yes, that's just what it's like. Like … I'm outside of myself.

Tom: Okay, now I want you to turn back around, as it's time for you to start this meeting. There are some things that need discussing and matters that need sorting out here, do you agree?

James: Oh yes, there certainly are.

Tom: So, now I want you to look over and, remembering that the objective of this meeting is to enhance the communication between all of these different parts of you, you are going to ask the *paranoid part*, the following question … *Paranoid part* … how can you help us all to increase the effectiveness of all of us parts as a whole? And as you ask that part of you that question you just listen to what he says … (I wait.)

James: It says, I'm not helping you. It sort of mumbles it, like it's sulking.

Tom: Okay, now I want you to look over at the *flirt part* of you and, as *flirt* has heard *paranoid*, what does it say back?

James: It says, why not?

Tom: And what does the *paranoid part* say back?

James: I just don't want to.

Tom: And then *fun part* speaks up. What does that say?

James: It says, this is ridiculous. You need to leave us alone.

I need to encourage my client that each part is important, to ensure that the process works effectively.

James: It's very cheeky the *paranoid part* now. It says again … I don't want to!

Tom: And then you hear *shy part* speak up, with something to say.

James: It says … okay, what do you want us to do?

James: They both (fun and flirt) say together … go on … just do it, just ask girls out.

Tom: And then you notice *lack of confidence* just turning their head slowly and saying something.

James: (Laughing.) It says … it's your fault *paranoid*.

Tom: And what does *paranoid* say?

James: It says … no it's not, it's your fault, you've no confidence, don't blame me.

Tom: And what does *shy* say as it hears that?

James: Don't blame him (lack of confidence) – you're the one who's paranoid!

Tom: And what does *flirt* say as it hears all this going on?

James: He says to *paranoid* … if you just let us get over this, we will, but you won't let that happen.

Tom: So *flirt* and the others would be able to overcome this if only *paranoid* would let them?

James: Yes.

Tom: So I want you to go back to you, yourself, sitting in that chair at the head of the table. And as you have heard this conversation, you know that *paranoid* is stopping the other parts of you overcoming this problem. You know that *shy* and *confidence* would be able to work at this, if only *paranoid* would let them. Now, as you are in charge of this meeting, what do you think would possibly help *fun* and *flirt*, *shy* and *lack of confidence*? What could they say to help *paranoid* let them feel free enough to approach someone for a date?

James: Well, they all need to say to *paranoid*, look you're not helping, you're not making us happy, whatever you're up to is of no benefit. It's just not helping.

Tom: So as you hear them say that to *paranoid*, how does *paranoid* react?

James: He just laughs and says, it's nothing to do with me. And then they all shout back at him … YES IT IS, and we've had enough!

Here I introduce into the dialogue another part of James's personality to begin a negotiation between the parts.

Tom: Now as you sit there you can become aware of another part entering into the room and that part takes a seat from the corner of the room and sits down at the table next to *paranoid*. This part of you is the *negotiator part*. Does this part have a name?

James: (Laughing.) Bond, James Bond! ... He's cool, he's looking at *paranoid* and smiling.

Tom: And what happens then?

James: He says to *paranoid* ... what do you need? He tells *Bond* that he isn't going to go away. It's important he stays here otherwise *confidence* might get *too* confident and then he will get hurt.

James begins to cry and I feel sad for the *hurt part* of him that seems to underpin the other parts. I encourage James to 'be' with the emotion, not needing to know what is happening for him but just acknowledging that he is experiencing it. It is important to remember that it is not our job to rescue the client from their feelings, rather to help them express them and just be there and hold the emotion.

Tom: Okay James, as you just become aware of how you feel, I just want you to listen now as *Bond* begins to tell *paranoid* how each of the different parts there at the table are here for the benefit of James as a whole, and that each of them is able to look out for James and do the best they can for him, and that includes you. But that this is not solely your job – this job is the responsibility of all the parts here. And as *Bond* tells *paranoid* this, what does *paranoid* say?

James: But what if that doesn't happen? I can't let *shy* get crushed again.

Tom: And what does *shy* say to this?

James: He is saying that if you keep running off each time, I'm never going to be able to learn to trust again. I just need some time to get used to girls again.

Tom: And what does *paranoid* say now?

James: That he might be able to stop, but he needs to know that the other parts are not going to abandon him.

Tom: Okay James, so I just want you now to listen to each part in turn as you look around the table, and just listen to what each part says to *paranoid*.

James: *Fun* talks now … and he says that he can still have fun. It doesn't mean that having fun will lead to hurt again.

Tom: And just check now what *paranoid* says to that.

James: He just nods his head.

Tom: And what does *flirt* say then?

James: He says that maybe he can cut down on his flirting and wonders if that would be helpful.

Tom: And what does *paranoid* say?

James: Yes, it would be, because then he will know more whether he really likes a girl or if he's just going through the motions of flirting.

Tom: Okay, and so now just notice what *lack of confidence* says next to *paranoid*.

James: He's not sure what to say really, he's a little shy … sometimes he just wants to run away.

Tom: And I wonder what might help *lack of confidence*?

James: I think he needs to know that *shy* can help him. If the two of them are helping each other and *fun* and *flirt* can be a little more cautious then he will be able to speak up.

Tom: Can the other parts do that?

James: Yes, they're nodding.

Tom: Great, so now *lack of confidence* can speak up, and what does that part say to *paranoid* now?

James: He says that if he can make an effort, then so can *paranoid*. Not every girl is out to hurt him and some are just as scared of being hurt as he was.

Note here the past tense, which can be a good indicator of something changing at an inner level.

Tom: And what does *paranoid* say back?

James: He sort of agrees, but it's going to take some getting used to. He's okay, just cautious; he still is paranoid, but not as much!

Tom: That's good, and I wonder now what *shy* would like to say?

James: (Smiling.) He's just sitting there, smiling. Like he has a little sparkle in his eye, almost mischievous. (James begins to laugh.)

Tom: Great … and I wonder if any part sitting around the table wants to say anything else now?

James: No, that's it, it feels good.

Tom: Great, James, so you can now bring the meeting to an end today, just reminding all of those parts that they have been doing a great job … and now that they are beginning to communicate even *more effectively*, whenever any part needs to have a voice, then they will be able to come to the meeting room and share their concerns with each other and find a way to help you feel more sure, aware and in touch with *all* parts of you. And now just watch all of those parts slowly leaving the room and, when the last one leaves, I want you to just turn around now, James, and look in the mirror.

James: It's me, wow! (Grinning.) I look okay, good, like I used to.

Tom: And how's that, James?

James: Like the old me, when I used to go up to girls and make friends and get to know them, before Lucy (his previous girlfriend). It feels good, I like it.

Tom: So James, knowing that you can come back into this meeting room whenever you want to, in the future, begin now just to let your mind become calm and clear and begin to bring yourself back into awareness and the room.

As we bring the hypnotic part of the session to an end, I wait for James to open his eyes.

Tom: How are you doing James?

James: That was weird! But really cool, it was like I saw all these different parts of me separately. And I never knew how they worked with each other. That was really strange!

Tom: And how does it feel to know that they can relate to each other and help each other now to have a voice and a presence in you?

James: Great, great. It's like I know that I'm cautious but that's okay. I can allow the shy part to be there but I can also have fun. It feels much more free.

We continued for a further ten minutes, exploring his experience and arranged a time for our next meeting.

Sandra: This technique demonstrates simplicity and yet profundity for the client as he learns what happens within him. There is just the right number of parts in the room – paranoid, fun, flirt, lack of confidence and shy – that relate to this client's specific issue. Bringing in too many parts could confuse both the client and the therapist, and would be too time consuming.

Tom manages the dialogue between the parts and also encourages James to be in control of the meeting. In this session, the paranoid part was reluctant to reveal its intentions or consider change, and this could have caused the dialogue to grind to a halt.

Tom successfully added another part, the negotiator, a useful part for us to remember when all parts are fighting and we need a voice of reason. It was at this stage that we gained greater insight as to the intention of the paranoid part: to keep lack of confidence from being too confident and getting hurt again. From this moment on, all parts were willing to participate in the dialogue to begin to look at how they could work more effectively together.

Tom moved towards a closure by checking that all parts were happy with what had been negotiated and that there was nothing left unsaid. I feel that James will not forget Bond in times of inner conflict and will use this essential negotiator to help resolve inner conflicts in future.

The Processing of the Session

This technique is one of my favourites, as it allows openness for what is important for the client in the session and it gives them a metaphorical structure – something that they can relate to which takes them outside of thinking about their 'problem' and into how best to resolve their internal conflicts.

In this session I introduced James to the parts of him he had described earlier and placed each part around the table. I brought each of them to an equal level, with James at the head of the table, assuming a position of authority. This allowed him to feel a sense of control over the individual parts, something that James had expressed he felt was lacking in his relationship with women.

After introducing the parts in the room, I asked James to imagine looking in the mirror behind him, with the intention of checking his self-concept. Here we saw the disconnection when he struggled even to see himself. What was helpful about this was that it allowed us to check later in the session how the parts work had impacted on him, and there had been a definite shift in his perception of himself, enabling him to see that a change had occurred.

In this session we started the dialogue with the paranoid part. In essence we could have started with any of the parts, because the focus here was not to find a *problem* part of the personality, but to create an internal dialogue and get the inner parts of James communicating with each other to find a solution.

From the moment I met James, I found myself reacting to him in a powerful way. I questioned his belief that women were definitely attracted to him, bearing in mind that he often presented with dirty, ill-fitting and ripped clothing and greasy unkempt hair.

It was not until *this* session that I felt myself warm to James; his defences relaxing, the parts of him that were causing his shyness uniting and my understanding of his struggle now much greater.

Sandra: Tom softened towards his client after this session and I wonder if in gaining greater understanding about fun, lack of confidence and paranoid, that greater rapport was beginning to be experienced. Seeing a client as more than just one part is often helpful, especially when we have clients that at first we just don't gel with or, dare I say, like.

What Happened Next?

At our next session, James described how he had started to feel differently about dating. He wasn't sure what it was, but just that something had shifted within him. He described feeling more connected with himself and now wanted to work on *keeping* these feelings. Over the next four sessions we worked on helping him to build this sense of confidence through suggestion therapy and imagery work, and also explored and worked on his self-esteem and self-image via NLP techniques. We ended therapy at a stage where he felt significantly more positive about this area of his life than when we had started, which was, for now, a success.

Sandra: It seems, as in many cases, that this session opened up both the therapy and the client, working at a more fundamental level of 'self', with the final sessions exploring self-esteem and self-image. James is well on his way to making the changes that he wants.

Epilogue

We hope you have been informed by the sharing of our journeys, the content of our sessions, the internal processes we went through and our reflections on each other's work. We personally have been challenged and excited by our discussions as it is not often that one gets the opportunity to reflect in detail on one's own work, let alone read, explore and challenge someone else's.

When we originally started writing this book we had a vision of providing many of our experiences encountered in training and as practising therapists, so as to help you, the reader, enjoy a smoother transition into the world of working therapeutically with clients, a world which we are both passionate about and love from deep within. As it turned out, this was an insurmountable task. What one encounters when entering into the field of helping others cannot be summed up in one book, and if anything we have been reminded that even after many years in practice we still have so much to learn.

As we came to finishing this book, we could have continued writing and re-writing, editing and even deleting chapters all over again, because we are constantly faced with the one source of knowledge that surpasses every training course, academic paper or book that we could ever experience, and that source of learning is our clients; the people who regularly present to us, bringing yet another perspective to life and hence a different approach that must be uniquely tailored to them as an individual.

Contentment for clients seems to come with having a sense of 'self', knowing who they are and how they are; for many this appears to be the goal of therapy. But this is, of course, a lifelong process and therapy offers the opportunity for individuals to begin to encounter themselves, steered by a skilled other to set them on their way.

We never forget the reason we do what we do – which we hope shows in the sharing of our clients' stories. The clients we encounter every day are those who teach us the most, in particular about the courage of being human.

In the time we have been writing this book we have both encountered the struggles of living and life that our clients regularly bring to therapy. We have been faced with dilemmas that have rocked us to our foundations and have made us question our existence, and indeed why we do what we do. We speak together daily about how the stories we hear remind us of the fragility of living, our own included. Yet one thing remains constant, and that is our unquestionable belief and faith that if we keep talking and exploring, if we keep applying what we know makes a difference, if we remain confident in the power of the human spirit to win over adversity, then we can and will live life to the best of our ability.

Glossary of Terms

Abreaction   An intense emotional reaction to a past experience. A release of 'out of awareness' emotional energy that is deemed, in part, to be causing the presenting problem (usually distress followed by tears).

Agoraphobia   A collection of phobias related to being in a variety of situations – shops, buses, trains, public places, etc. Situations are avoided when on one's own. Often related to panic attacks.

Anchoring   An NLP term. This is where a stimulus gets connected to and sets off a response. This can be naturally occurring and result from a previous experience (a dog sets off anxiety if you have previously been bitten by one) or deliberately created (the door to an exam room triggering feelings of confidence).

Artfully vague   Language that is general, ambiguous and metaphoric.

Associated   When someone is associated into an experience, they are experiencing it as if they are looking out of their own eyes, they are in their own body and they are feeling it as if it is happening now.

Auditory digital   A representational system that is our 'thought talk' and looks to make logical sense of the world being experienced. Problems are worked out in the mind rather than by holding the world in pictures, sounds or feelings.

Base subconscious   Our body's natural reactions and physiological functioning: heart rate, bladder control, place of healing if we break a bone or have a cold, etc.

Bracketing   A process of putting aside our presuppositions and assumptions about something or someone.

Changing memory   The brain determines the parameters of our experiences via submodalities; by changing the submodalities it is possible to change how a memory is held.

Chunking down   A changing perception process through allowing language to become more specific.

Chunking up   A changing perception process through allowing language to become more general.

Clenched fist   A self-anchoring technique that uses the hands to anchor a desired state so that it can be triggered off at any time; similarly an un-resourceful state can be simultaneously collapsed.

Conscious   Everything in awareness in 'the moment'.

Core beliefs   Generalisations that we believe to be true about ourselves, about others and about the world. These guide us in how we perceive and make sense of experiences and of reality. Core beliefs are closely linked to values.

Deconstruct   Breaking an experience down via the use of modalities and submodalities.

Desired outcome   A specific result that is wished for and is built up using modalities and submodalities.

Dissociated   When someone is dissociated from an experience, they are watching themselves from the outside – as if they are watching themselves in a film.

Existential approach   A philosophical way of working that focuses on life: what it means to be alive and the purpose and meaning of existence. It embraces human issues such as life and death, isolation and relatedness, uncertainty and anxiety.

Future pacing   Mentally rehearsing and imagining a scenario happening in the future. It is used to test and/or practice a desired outcome.

GAI   Guided affective imagery.

Gestalt   A psychology that focuses on human perception being a whole pattern, rather than a collection of individual parts.

Individuation   From analytical psychology: the process through which the personality becomes integrated into a well-functioning whole and a person becomes his/her 'true self'.

Intrapersonal   Communication that happens internally within the mind, as opposed to with another person (interpersonal).

Introjection   In object relations theory, objects (or other people) are taken in and become part of the individual's beliefs and values (super-ego).

Kinaesthetic   The feelings and sensations (physical/emotional) of our experiences.

Meta model   An NLP model based on language patterns that hide the deeper meaning of what we are saying. By questioning the deletions, distortions and generalisations in our language, deeper meanings can be revealed.

Milton model   The opposite to the meta model: using vague language patterns (including generalisations, deletions and distortions) to pace another person's experience.

Miracle day   A visualisation that takes the client through a day where their symptoms are no longer with them. It allows for the imagining of such possibilities, exciting the mind as to what *can* be.

Modality   A sensory system in which we code information: visual, auditory, kinaesthetic, olfactory and gustatory.

NLP   Neurolinguistic programming. A model of how we structure and programme (neurologically and linguistically) our interpersonal experiences based on the study of successful patterns of mental and emotional behaviour.

Parent/adult/child   The transactional analysis theory of how we hold parent, adult and child parts within us and refer/resort to them when relating to others.

Parts Subpersonalities that operate within us (e.g. angry, critical). The parts approach believes that symptoms originate from conflicting or over-inflated parts.

Perceptual positions The view we take at any one time. This can be from our own (first position), from the other (second position) or from an observer (third position).

Phonological ambiguity Two words that sound the same (here, hear; where/we're; know/no) but which can be interpreted differently.

PPR Passive progressive relaxation. A long hypnotic induction that takes the client through slow physical bodily relaxation, concentrating on specific parts of the body at any one given time.

Project An existential theory (Jean-Paul Sartre, 1905–1980) of how we internally plan our life events and stories.

Psychosomatic A physical illness with psychological roots.

Rapid induction Based on fast relaxation. The premise is that sufficient relaxation is achieved quickly as soon as the eyes are closed, and the deeper the relaxation the client allows themselves to be in, the more suggestible they are.

Regression A technique to return to a younger/immature stage of life in order to find the source of a symptom and release the emotional charge of the unrealised memory.

Reparative A process of repair, meaning a type of re-parenting.

Resourceful A neurological and physical experience of capability and competence.

Stacking Setting up a chain of anchored desired states one after the other so that they can be fired and linked at the same time. Multiple anchored states are more powerful than a single anchor.

Subconscious Everything not in our present awareness.

Submodality   The finer detail within a modality or the quality of our representational system (e.g. within the visual modality, a submodality would include colour/monochrome, near/far, panoramic/detailed, near/distant, etc.).

Suggestion therapy   Once in a hypnotic state, the therapist uses statements that are designed to influence the client's behaviour. There are direct suggestions ('cigarettes will taste like x') and indirect suggestions ('and you can notice how much easier it is to breathe, how food has more flavour').

SWISH   A technique that substitutes memories and/or images. A cue from the unwanted problem state is chained to the desired/ wanted state.

Temporality   A philosophical term to describe the way time is. The traditional mode of temporality is a linear progression of past, present and future.

Theatre screen   An NLP technique that uses the movie of an undesired response and deconstructs it via reversing it and altering the submodalities.

Timing and pacing   Building rapport over a period of time by becoming aware of where the other is and where you are in the experience.

Trance   An altered internally focused state of awareness.

Trigger   That which initiates a specific behavioural response.

Utilisation   Using the resources that are already within the person and being able to call upon the required internal states when needed.

World view   A person's fundamental existential themes, values, emotions and ethics.

References

Ader, R. (2006) *Psychoneuroimmunology*, 2 vols. London: Academic Press.

Bandler, R. (1985) *Using Your Brain for a Change: Neuro-Linguistic Programming*. Moab, UT: Real People Press.

Bandler, R. and Grinder, J. (1979) *Frogs into Princes: Neuro Linguistic Programming*. Moab, UT: Real People Press.

Barnett, E. (1979) *Unlock Your Mind and Be Free!* Glendale, CA: Westwood Publishing.

Berne, E. (1986) *Transactional Analysis in Psychotherapy*. New York: Ballantine Books.

Cheek, D. and Rossi, E. (1988) *Mind–Body Therapy: Methods of Ideodynamic Healing in Hypnosis*. New York: W.W. Norton.

Clarkson, P. (1999) *Gestalt Counselling in Action*. London: Sage.

Daruna, J. (2004) *Introduction to Psychoneuroimmunology*. London: Academic Press.

Dilts, R. (1983) *Applications of Neuro-Linguistic Programming*. Cupertino, CA: Meta Publications.

Elman, D. (1984) *Hypnotherapy*. Glendale, CA: Westwood Publishing.

Emmerson, G. (2007) *Ego State Therapy*. Carmarthen: Crown House Publishing.

Erickson, M. (1984) *Healing in Hypnosis*. Vol. 1, *Seminars, Workshops, and Lectures of Milton H. Erickson*. New York: Irvington Publishers.

Erickson, M., Rossi, E. and O'Ryan, M. (1986) *Mind–Body Communication in Hypnosis*. New York: Irvington Publishers.

Federn, P. (1960) *Ego Psychology and the Psychoses*. New York: Basic Books.

Freud, S. (1900 [1997]) *The Interpretation of Dreams*. Ware: Wordsworth.

Freud, S. and Breuer, J. (1895 [1984]) *Studies on Hysteria*. New York: Penguin Classics.

Hammond, D. C. (1990) *Handbook of Hypnotic Suggestions and Metaphors*. New York: W.W. Norton.

Hay, L. (1982) *Heal Your Body*. London: Hay House.

Hay, L. (1984) *You Can Heal Your Life*. London: Hay House.

Hunter, R. (2005) *Hypnosis for Inner Conflict Resolution: Introducing Parts Therapy*. Carmarthen: Crown House Publishing.

Jung, C. G. and Jaffé, A. (1962 [1995]) *Memories, Dreams, Reflections*. London: Fontana Press.

Kendall-Tackett, K. (2009) *The Psychoneuroimmunology of Chronic Disease: Exploring the Links between Inflammation, Stress, and Illness*. Washington, DC: American Psychological Association.

Kretschmer, B. (1922) *Medizinische Psychologie*. Stuttgart: Thieme.

Leuner, H. (1954 [1984]) *Guided Affective Imagery: Mental Imagery in Short-Term Psychotherapy: The Basic Course*. New York: Thieme-Stratton.

Leuner, H. (1966) Abbreviation of a lecture given at the New Jersey Neuropsychiatric Institute, Princeton, NJ, 16 May 1966. Reprinted in *American Journal of Psychotherapy* 23(1) (1969): 4–22.

Mason, K. (2000) *Thoughts that Harm, Thoughts that Heal*. London: Piatkus.

Muss, D. (1991) *The Trauma Trap*. London: Doubleday.

Quigley, D. (1987) *Alchemical Hypnotherapy: A Manual of Practical Technique*. Redway, CA: Lost Coast Press.

Rossi, E. L. (1986) *The Psychobiology of Mind–Body Healing: New Concepts of Therapeutic Hypnosis*. New York: W.W. Norton.

Rowan, J. (1990) *Subpersonalities: The People Inside Us*. New York: Routledge.

Schedlowski, M. and Tewes, U. (1999) *Psychoneuroimmunology: An Interdisciplinary Introduction*. New York: Springer.

Schoettle, U. C. (1980) Guided imagery: A tool in child psychotherapy. *American Journal of Psychotherapy* 34(2): 220–227.

Schorr, J. (1972) *Psycho-Imagination Therapy: The Integration of Phenomenology and Imagination*. New York: Intercontinental Medical Book Corp.

Shapiro, D. (2005) *Your Body Speaks Your Mind: Decoding the Emotional, Psychological, and Spiritual Messages that Underlie Illness*. Louisville, CO: Sounds True, Inc.

Stein, C. (1963) The clenched fist technique as a hypnotic procedure in clinical psychotherapy. *American Journal of Clinical Hypnosis* 6: 113–119.

Stone, H. and Stone, S. (1998) *Embracing Ourselves: The Voice Dialogue Manual*. Mill Valley, CA: Nataraj Publishing.

Tebbetts, C. (1993) *Self Hypnosis and Other Mind Expanding Techniques*. Glendale, CA: Westwood Publishing.

Utay, J. and Miller, M. (2006) Guided imagery as an effective therapeutic technique: A brief review of its history and efficacy research. *Journal of Instructional Psychology* 33(1): 40–43.

Watkins, J. (1971) The affect bridge: A hypnoanalytic technique. *International Journal of Clinical and Experimental Hypnosis* 19(1): 21–27.

Watkins, H. and Watkins, J. (1997) *Ego States: Theory and Therapy*. New York: W.W. Norton.

Index